Digital Electronics for Technicians

Digital Electronics for Technicians

D C Green
M Tech, CEng, MIEE

Longman
Scientific &
Technical

Longman Group UK Limited,
Longman House, Burnt Mill, Harlow,
Essex CM20 2JE, England
and Associated Companies throughout the world.

First published 1980 under the title *Digital Techniques
and Systems* by Pitman Publishing Limited
Second edition 1982
Third edition 1988
Fourth edition 1993

British Library Cataloguing in Publication Data

Green, D.C.
  Digital electronics for technicians.
  4th ed.
  1. Digital electronics
  I. Title   II. Green, D.C. Digital
  techniques and systems
  621.3815   TK7868.D5

ISBN 0−582−21796−2

Printed in Malaysia by PA

Set by 4 in 10/12pt Times

Contents

Preface

This book provides a comprehensive coverage of the basic techniques used in modern digital electronics. The treatment is such that the book constitutes a suitable first course in the subject for technicians.

The UK Business and Technician Education Council (BTEC) scheme for the education of electronic and telecommunication technicians introduces the student to the concepts of digital electronics at both the second and the third levels. This book has been written to provide a complete coverage of the digital part of the Electronics NII unit and of the level three unit Digital Electronics NIII.

Chapter 1 provides a basic introduction to some of the many and varied uses of digital techniques in modern technology and is intended to give the newcomer to the field some idea of the many possibilities associated with the use of modern digital circuitry. Chapters 2,3 and 4 cover the subject of electronic gates of all kinds; Chapter 2 discusses the various kinds of gate, e.g. AND and OR, and some of the ways that they can be interconnected to perform various logical functions. Chapter 3 discusses the simplification of Boolean equations using both algebraic and mapping methods. Chapter 4 introduces the various logic families with particular emphasis being placed upon TTL and CMOS logic. The next three chapters deal with, respectively, MSI combinational logic circuits, flip-flops, and counters.

The remainder of the book is concerned with flip-flops and their use in counters and shift registers, semiconductor memories, and visual displays. The book concludes with an introduction to the interfacing of digital equipment to the analogue world by the use of analogue-to-digital and digital-to-analogue converters.

The book has been written on the assumption that the reader will possess a knowledge of electronics and of electrical principles equivalent to that reached by the BTEC level II student, since a knowledge of integrated circuits is throughout taken for granted.

Some worked examples are included in the text to illustrate the principles that have been discussed and a number of exercises are provided at the end of the book. Answers to numerical problems are given.

D.C.G.

1 Digital Systems

Much present-day electronic and telecommunication equipment is still analogue in nature. This means that the signals to be handled, processed or transmitted are represented by voltages whose amplitude and/or frequency vary continuously with time; thus, in a telephone system, the transmitted signals are replicas of the speech waveforms. Many examples of analogue equipment are well known; for example, the radio and television receivers to be found in the majority of homes.

Digital signals are not continuous in nature but consist of discrete pulses of voltage or current, known as *bits*, which represent the information to be processed. Digital voltages can vary only in discrete steps; normally only two voltage levels are used — one of which is zero — so that two-state devices can be employed. A two-stage device is one which has only two stable states; so that it is either ON or it is OFF. Examples of two-state devices are: a lamp which is either glowing visibly or it is not; a buzzer which is either producing an audible sound or not; or an electrical switch which either completes an electrical circuit or breaks it. In digital electronics the two-state devices that are used are the semiconductor diode and the transistor, both bipolar and field effect.

The advantages to be gained from the use of digital techniques instead of analogue methods arise largely from the use of just the two voltage levels. Digital circuitry operates by switching transistors ON and OFF and does not need to produce or to detect precise values of voltage and/or current at particular points in an equipment or system. Because of this it is easier and cheaper to mass-produce digital circuitry. Also, the binary nature of the signals makes it much easier to consistently obtain a required operating performance from a large number of circuits. Digital circuits are generally more reliable than analogue circuits because faults will not often occur through variations in performance caused by changing values of components, misaligned coils, and so on. Again, the effects of noise and interference are very much reduced in a digital system since the digital pulses can always be regenerated and made like new whenever their waveshape is becoming distorted to the point where errors are likely. This is not possible in an analogue system where the effect of unwanted noise and interference signals is to permanently degrade the signal.

There are two main reasons why both electronics and telecommunications have been mainly analogue in nature until recent years. First, digital circuitry was, in the main, not economic until integrated circuits became freely available, and, secondly, the transmission of digital signals requires the provision of circuits with a very wide bandwidth. Some digital circuits and equipments have, of course, been available since pre-integrated circuit days but their scope and application were very limited.

The Digital Computer and the Microprocessor

Nowadays the digital computer is an integral part of the day-to-day operation of many firms and organizations, ranging from Government departments, commercial concerns such as banks and insurance companies, to industrial firms in all branches of engineering and science. Computers are employed for the calculation of wages and salaries, taxes, pensions, bills and accounts; for the storage of medical, scientific and engineering data; and for the rapid booking of aircraft seats, theatre tickets and foreign holidays. Computers are also used to carry out complex scientific and engineering calculations, to control engineering processes in factories, to control the operation of telephone exchanges and military equipment and weapons, to control the distribution networks for gas, water and electricity, and for many other purposes.

A digital computer is able to store large quantities of data in its memory which can be made available as and when required. The task to be performed by the computer is detailed to the computer by means of a set of instructions known as the *program*. The program is fed into the computer and stored in another part of its memory.

The basic block diagram of a digital computer is shown in Fig. 1.1. The instructions contained in the program are taken sequentially (one after the other) from the memory under the direction of the control unit. Each instruction causes the arithmetic unit to perform arithmetic and logic operations on the data, also taken from the memory. The results of the calculations can be stored in the memory or they can be held temporarily in a part of the arithmetic unit known as an accumulator. When a calculation has been completed, the control unit

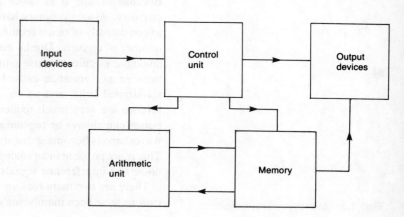

Fig. 1.1 Digital computer

will transfer the results to an output device, which will (probably) produce the results in printed form; alternatively, a vdu may be employed or the results may be transmitted over a *data link* to a distant point where they are needed.

The input devices used to feed information into a computer are usually some kind of keyboard, tape recorder or disc drive.

Minicomputers and Microcomputers

A minicomputer has a smaller storage capability than a mainframe computer but the capacity provided is adequate for very many applications. A minicomputer is small enough physically to be brought into an office, often on a trolley, when it is needed, plugged into the electric mains supply, and then used. Minicomputers are also used as relatively inexpensive means of controlling industrial systems and processes. Microcomputers are smaller still, and correspondingly cheaper, and include the personal computers often found in the home.

Microprocessors

The term microprocessor is generally applied to a form of integrated circuit that is able to control the operation of a wide variety of equipments. A microprocessor can be built into the equipment whose operation it is to control. Figure 1.2 shows the basic block diagram of a microprocessor system; the microprocessor chip contains various registers, an arithmetic unit and control circuitry. The memory and the input/output interface circuits are also provided by integrated circuits.

As an example, microprocessor control of modern radio receivers and systems is increasingly used in the latest equipments. A microprocessor can be programmed to control the tuning, the gain and the selectivity of a receiver as the receiving conditions alter. Remote h.f. radio stations can be distantly controlled by means of a microprocessor; the functions controlled being the selection of the frequency

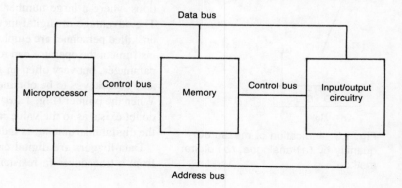

Fig. 1.2 Microprocessor system

to be transmitted and the frequency to be received as determined by a pre-set schedule. Also, the performance of the station can be monitored and any faults or degradation of service detected and recorded.

Another example is the type of automatic washing machines which go through their washing cycle under the control of an in-built microprocessor.

Digital Equipment and Systems

Hand-calculators are nowadays in common use and provide another example of the use of digital circuitry. All calculators are able to carry out the basic mathematical procedures while many are provided with several more advanced mathematical facilities. Some models are programmable. The circuitry contained within a calculator is complex and these devices have only become practical since the advent of integrated circuits.

Many cash registers and weighing scales used in the shops are electronic and these provide a readout in digital form of the total money to be paid and, once the money offered has been entered by the operator, of the change to be given, as well as a printout of the purchases. A point-of-sale terminal also keeps a record of the total cash input and in some cases this is signalled to a central point where a complete record for the shop or department can be maintained. The input data to an EPoS terminal is often entered by means of a bar-code scanner. The terminal incorporates a price look-up table which stores the price of each item sold and automatically displays the cost of each item. Often a microprocessor is also involved so that records are automatically kept of the items sold, and of the stock left on the shelves and in the store. This enables the management to know at all times the stocks held of all items so that re-stocking can be carried out in ample time. It is possible to programme the microprocessor to order from the warehouse those items whose stocks are falling below an appointed figure.

In engineering, digital readouts of data are often more convenient and accurate than analogue readings. Digital voltmeters and frequency meters or counters are particularly suited to measurement applications where a large number of repetitive readings are to be made. The advantage of digital meters is most noticeable when relatively unskilled personnel are employed to carry out the tests. With a digital instrument the operator can read at a glance the value of the displayed parameter, but very often an analogue reading requires care if reasonable accuracy is to be obtained. This point is illustrated by Fig. 1.3. When the pointer (Fig. 1.3a) is in between two scale markings, some doubt exists as to the value indicated. No such doubt is present with the digital instrument; its indicated value (Fig. 1.3b) is easy to read.

Data-loggers are digital circuits that convert the analogue output from a transducer (a resistance strain gauge, a thermocouple, or a

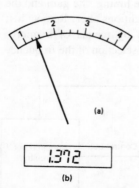

Fig. 1.3 Indication of measured quantity by (a) analogue, (b) digital method

Data-loggers are digital circuits that convert the analogue output from a transducer (a resistance strain gauge, a thermocouple, or a potentiometer, for example) into a digital form so that the measured parameter can be recorded on a magnetic tape.

Another application of computers and digital techniques that is gaining in importance in the modern world is in the field of transport. The movement of vehicles in a large transport system can be controlled and monitored by a computer. British Rail, for example, have introduced a computerized system for the optimized control of its freight traffic. Each truck has its movements continuously monitored and the computer works out and augments the best way of moving the trucks around the network in order to carry the maximum amount of freight in the most economic manner. In many large cities, computers control the traffic lights that direct the flow of traffic across road junctions. The computer continuously monitors the number of cars passing and waiting to pass the various junctions and varies the frequency of the traffic light operations to optimize the flow of traffic.

Electronic fund transfer is commonly employed to move money from one bank account to another and bank/building society wall cash dispensers are well known.

Telephone Transmission Systems

Telecommunication systems have traditionally been analogue in nature. Speech signals can be transmitted over purely analogue circuits routed over a combination of physical pairs in telephone cables and frequency division multiplex channels over line and/or radio links. Digital transmission using *pulse code modulation* is increasingly used and much of the telephone network in the United Kingdom now uses this technique. The telephone networks of many countries are being converted to use digital techniques with an Integrated Services Digital Network (ISDN) being the eventual target. ISDN is to be an integrated telephone network in which junction and trunk transmission, signalling and exchange switching are all to be achieved using digital methods. One advantage of digital working is that it can be used for all kinds of signal, be it speech, music, television, telegraphy or data.

The distribution of the frequency-modulated vhf sound broadcast signals and the audio signals of television broadcasts from studios to transmitters is carried out digitally using pulse code modulation. Teletext services are now transmitted by both the BBC and the IBA — using the names CEEFAX and ORACLE respectively — to provide information to the home. The data is transmitted digitally using some of the lines in each field of the television signal which are not modulated by the video signal. In the television receiver a digital decoder is provided to recover and display the incoming information on the television screen. A similar kind of information service, known as PRESTEL, has been introduced by British Telecom. The data is transmitted, again in digital form, over a telephone line to the home and, after decoding, is displayed by the television receiver.

Private mobile radio systems operating in the vhf and the uhf bands

bands can also be controlled by a computer to ensure the optimum performance as the mobiles move around the service area. Such systems are used by organizations that employ a large number of mobiles, such as British Gas in the UK. A public mobile radio system, integrated with the telephone network and known as cellular radio, also depends upon computer control.

2 Electronic Gates

An electronic gate is a circuit that is able to operate on a number of input binary signals in order to perform a particular logical function. The logic gate is one of the basic building blocks from which many different kinds of logic system can be constructed. Electronic gates are readily available in integrated circuit form and the various logic families in common use will be discussed and their characteristics compared in another chapter. In this chapter the emphasis will be on the various types of gates and the ways in which they can be interconnected to perform different logical functions. The types of gate to be considered are the AND, NOT, OR, NAND, NOR, exclusive-OR, and the exclusive-NOR or coincidence gate. The IEC (International Electrotechnical Commission) symbols for each of these gates are given in Fig. 2.1. The American gate symbols are also given. Positive logic is assumed throughout this chapter; that is, logic 1 is represented by the more-positive voltage, and logic 0 by the less-positive voltage, of two possible values.

The AND Gate

Figure 2.2 shows a lamp connected in series with two switches, S_1 and S_2, and a battery. For a current to flow in the circuit and the lamp to light both S_1 *and* S_2 must be closed. A switch when open, or OFF, is denoted by logic 0 and when closed, or ON, is represented by logic 1, while the state of the lamp when it is lit is given by logic 1 and when unlit by logic 0. The operation of the circuit can then be described by its **truth table** (see Table 2.1).

The action of the circuit can also be described by the Boolean equation:

$$L = S_1 \cdot S_2 \tag{2.1}$$

The dot $\cdot$ is the Boolean symbol for the AND logical function but it is often omitted. Equation (2.1) states that, for the lamp L to be ON or 1, both S_1 *and* S_2 must be ON or 1.

The AND gate is a logic element having two or more input terminals and only one output terminal. The output logic state is 1 only when *all* of the inputs are at logic 1. If any one or more of the inputs is at logic 0, the output state will also be at logic 0. Using Boolean algebra the output F of an AND gate with three inputs A, B, and C can be written down as

$$F = ABC \tag{2.2}$$

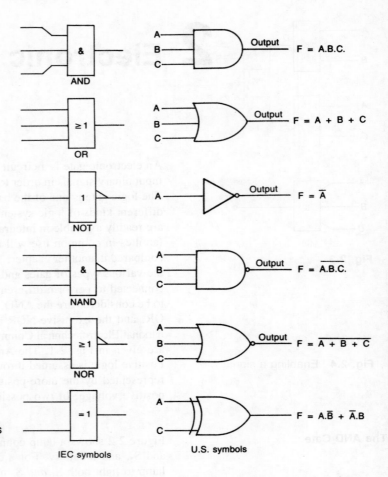

Fig. 2.1 Gate symbols. ($\vdash$ denotes active-low output; $\dashv$ denotes active-low input)

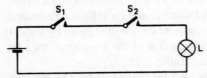

Fig. 2.2 The AND logic function

Table 2.1

Switch S_1	0	1	0	1
Switch S_2	0	0	1	1
Lamp L	0	0	0	1

Table 2.2 AND gate

A	0	1	0	0	1	1	0	1
B	0	0	1	0	1	0	1	1
C	0	0	0	1	0	1	1	1
F	0	0	0	0	0	0	0	1

The inputs *A*, *B* and *C* are known as the input variables or *literals*.

The operation of any logical element can be described by means of a truth table; this is a table which shows the output state of the circuit for all the possible combinations of input states. The truth table of a 3-input AND gate is given by Table 2.2. It is clear from the table that the output is 1 only when *A* AND *B* AND *C* are 1.

Note that the number of combinations of the input variables is equal to 2^n, where *n* is the number of variables. Thus, the truth table of a 4-input AND gate would require 2^4 (or 16) columns, and so on.

EXAMPLE 2.1

Figure 2.3*a* shows a digital circuit constructed using AND gates. Write down the truth table of the circuit. Simplify the circuit.

Solution
The truth table is given by Table 2.3. This truth table is the same as Table 2.2, hence the required logical function could be produced by a single 3-input AND gate as shown in Fig. 2.3*b*.

This is the first indication that it is often possible to simplify a logic circuit.

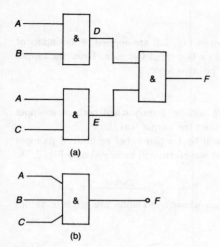

Fig. 2.3

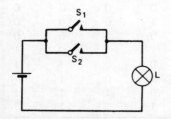

Fig. 2.4 Enabling a signal

Table 2.3

A	B	$D = A \cdot B$	C	$E = A \cdot C$	$F = DE = ABC$
0	0	0	0	0	0
1	0	0	0	0	0
0	1	0	0	0	0
1	1	1	0	0	0
0	0	0	1	0	0
1	0	0	1	1	0
0	1	0	1	0	0
1	1	1	1	1	1

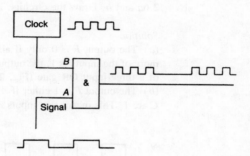

The AND gate can be used to *enable* and *inhibit* a digital signal. Since the output of a 2-input AND gate will be 1 only if both its inputs A and B are 1, a control signal applied to, say, input A can control the passage of a signal applied to input B. When input A is at the logic 0 level, it will stop, or **inhibit**, the signal at B from passing through the gate. When input A is at logic 1, it will allow, or **enable**, the signal applied to B to pass to the output. Very often the control signal is a regularly occurring pulse waveform derived from a circuit known as the *clock*. An example of this technique is shown in Fig. 2.4.

The OR Gate

Current will flow in the circuit shown in Fig. 2.5 and light the lamp if either switch S_1 OR switch S_2 OR both S_1 and S_2 are closed or ON. Table 2.4 is the truth table for this circuit.

The Boolean equation describing the action of the circuit is

$$L = S_1 + S_2 \tag{2.3}$$

The + sign is the symbol for the logical function OR.

An OR gate has two or more input terminals and a single output terminal which will be at logic 1 whenever any one or more of its input terminals is at logic 1. The Boolean expression for the output of a 3-input OR gate is given by equation (2.4).

$$F = A + B + C \tag{2.4}$$

The truth table of a 3-input OR gate is given by Table 2.5.

Fig. 2.5 The OR logic function

Table 2.4

Switch S_1	0	1	0	1
Switch S_2	0	0	1	1
Lamp	0	1	1	1

Table 2.5 OR gate

A	0	1	0	0	1	1	0	1
B	0	0	1	0	1	0	1	1
C	0	0	0	1	0	1	1	1
F	0	1	1	1	1	1	1	1

EXAMPLE 2.2

The rectangular waveforms shown in Fig. 2.6 are applied to the inputs of (a) a two-input AND gate and (b) a two-input OR gate. Draw the output waveform of each gate. Assume positive logic.

Solution
(a) The output of the AND gate will be 1 only when both of its input waveforms are 1. Figure 2.7a shows the output waveform.
(b) The output of the OR gate will be 1 when either or both of its input waveforms are 1. Hence the output waveform will be as given by Fig. 2.7b.

EXAMPLE 2.3

Determine the types of logic circuit whose truth tables are given in Tables 2.6a and b. Draw the circuits.

Solution
(a) The output F is 0 only if all three inputs A, B and C are 0. If one or more of the inputs is 1, the output is 1. Hence, Table 2.6a is the truth table of a three-input OR gate (Fig. 2.8a).
(b) The output F is 1 either if A and B are 1 *or* if C is 1 *or* if A and B and C are 1. This means that inputs A and B are connected to a two-input AND

Fig. 2.6

Fig. 2.7

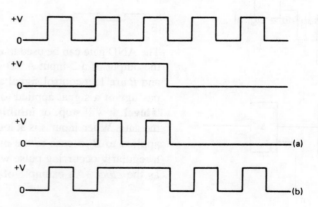

Table 2.6

| (a) | | | | (b) | | | |
A	B	C	F	A	B	C	F
0	0	0	0	0	0	0	0
1	0	0	1	1	0	0	0
0	1	0	1	0	1	0	0
0	0	1	1	1	1	0	1
1	1	0	1	0	0	1	1
1	0	1	1	1	0	1	1
0	1	1	1	0	1	1	1
1	1	1	1	1	1	1	1

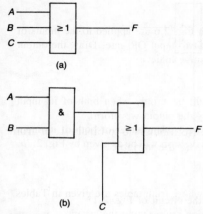

Fig. 2.8

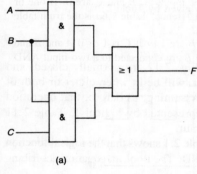

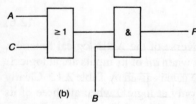

Fig. 2.9

The NOT Gate

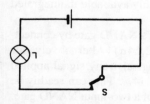

Fig. 2.10 The NOT function

gate whose output is applied, with input C, to a two-input OR gate (see Fig. 2.8b).

EXAMPLE 2.4

(a) Write down the Boolean equations that describe the logic circuits given in Figs 2.9a and b. (b) Write down the truth table for each circuit and compare them. Comment on the results.

Solution

(a) For circuit a, $F = A \cdot B + B \cdot C$ and for circuit b, $F = (A + C) \cdot B$. (b) The truth table for circuit a is given by Table 2.7 and the truth table for circuit b is Table 2.8.

Comparing the rows in the tables that give the outputs F of the two circuits it can be seen that they are identical. This shows that the same logical function can often be produced by different combinations of gates. In this example, circuit b requires only two gates to perform the desired function as opposed to the three gates needed by circuit a, and so circuit b would probably be chosen.

Table 2.7

A	0	1	0	0	1	1	0	1
B	0	0	1	0	1	0	1	1
AB	0	0	0	0	1	0	0	1
C	0	0	0	1	0	1	1	1
BC	0	0	0	0	0	0	1	1
F	0	0	0	0	1	0	1	1

Table 2.8

A	0	1	0	0	1	1	0	1
B	0	0	1	0	1	0	1	1
C	0	0	0	1	0	1	1	1
$A + C$	0	1	0	1	1	1	1	1
F	0	0	0	0	1	0	1	1

The NOT logical function is performed by the circuit in Fig. 2.10. Before the switch S_1 is operated, current flows in the circuit and the lamp is lit, or ON. Operation of the switch stops current flowing in the circuit and turns the lamp OFF. The truth table for this circuit is given by Table 2.9.

The Boolean equation for the circuit is

$$L = \bar{S} \tag{2.5}$$

The bar over a symbol means 'NOT that symbol'. In the equation, it means 'NOT S'. The NOT gate is often known as an inverter. The hex inverter consists of six inverters in one integrated circuit package.

Table 2.9

S	0	1
L	1	0

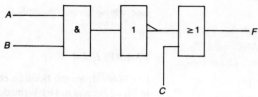

Fig. 2.11

Table 2.10

A	0	1	0	1	0	1	0	1
B	0	0	1	1	0	0	1	1
$A \cdot B$	0	0	0	1	0	0	0	1
$\overline{A \cdot B}$	1	1	1	0	1	1	1	0
C	0	0	0	0	1	1	1	1
F	1	1	1	0	1	1	1	1

Inverting the value of a variable from binary 0 to binary 1, or from 1 to 0, is known as *complementing* the variable.

EXAMPLE 2.5

(*a*) Write down the truth table of the circuit of Fig. 2.11.
(*b*) Write down the Boolean equation representing the circuit.

Solution
(*a*) The truth table of the circuit is given by Table 2.10.
(*b*) $F = \overline{A \cdot B} + C$ (*Ans.*)

The NAND Gate

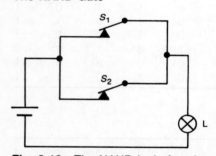

Fig. 2.12   The NAND logic function

Table 2.11

S_1	0	1	0	1
S_2	0	0	1	1
L	1	1	1	0

Table 2.12   NAND gate

A	0	1	0	1	0	1	0	1
B	0	0	1	1	0	0	1	1
C	0	0	0	0	1	1	1	1
F	1	1	1	1	1	1	1	0

The two switches S_1 and S_2 in Fig. 2.12 are normally closed, and open when operated. The lamp L will be lit when either or both of the switches are non-operated. Assuming, as before, that operation of a switch or of the lamp is represented by logical 1, Table 2.11 gives the truth table for the circuit.

Comparing Table 2.11 with Table 2.1 shows that the logical function performed is NOT AND, or NAND. The Boolean equation describing the operation of the circuit is

$$L = \overline{S_1 S_2} \tag{2.6}$$

The NAND gate performs the inverse of the AND logical function, so that its output is at logic 0 only when *all* of its inputs are at logic 1. The truth table of a 3-input NAND gate is given by Table 2.12. Clearly the output of the NAND gate is only at logic 0 when all three of its inputs are at logic 1. This action can be described by the Boolean expression

$$F = \overline{ABC} \tag{2.7}$$

The NAND function can be produced by an AND gate followed by a NOT gate (Fig. 2.13*a*) but it is most often produced by a NAND gate (Fig. 2.13*b*). The NAND gate is readily available in integrated circuit form.

The NOT function can be obtained using a NAND gate by connecting its input terminals together (see Fig. 2.14*a*). Alternatively, for a two-input gate, if one input is held at logical 1 any signal applied to the other input will be inverted, Fig. 2.14*b*. This can readily be confirmed by writing down the truth table of a two-input NAND gate.

Fig. 2.13 The NAND function produced by (a) an AND gate followed by an inverter, (b) a NAND gate

A B C | & | ABC → ≥1 → $\overline{ABC}$

(a)

A B C | & | $\overline{ABC}$

(b)

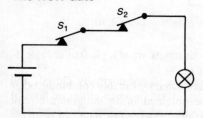

A | & | $\overline{A}$

(a)

Logic 1 voltage level

A | & | $\overline{A}$

(b)

Fig. 2.14 The NAND gate connected as an inverter

The NOR Gate

Fig. 2.15 The NOR logic function

Table 2.13

S_1	0	1	0	1
S_2	0	0	1	1
L	1	0	0	0

Table 2.14 NOR gate

A	0	1	0	0	1	1	0	1
B	0	0	1	0	1	0	1	1
C	0	0	0	1	0	1	1	1
F	1	0	0	0	0	0	0	0

The Exclusive-OR Gate

The NOR (NOT OR) logical function is performed by the circuit given in Fig. 2.15. Clearly, only if both switches are non-operated will current flow in the circuit and the lamp light. Table 2.13 gives the truth table, and equation (2.8) the Boolean equation, describing the logical operation of the circuit.

$$L = \overline{S_1 + S_2} \tag{2.8}$$

The NOR gate performs the same logical function as an OR gate that is followed by an inverter. This means that its output is at logic 0 whenever any one or more of its inputs is at logic 1. The truth table of a 3-input NOR gate is given by Table 2.14 and the Boolean equation describing the function is given by expression (2.9).

$$F = \overline{A + B + C} \tag{2.9}$$

The NOR gate can be used as an *inverter* or NOT gate by connecting its inputs together (Fig. 2.16a) or by connecting one input to logic 0 (Fig. 2.16b).

EXAMPLE 2.6

The waveforms shown in Fig. 2.17a and b are applied to (a) a 2-input AND gate, (b) a 2-input OR gate, (c) a 2-input NOR gate, and (d) a 2-input NAND gate. For each case draw the output waveform of the gate.

Solution
The required waveforms are shown in Figs 2.17c, d, e, and f respectively.

The exclusive-OR gate has just two input terminals and one output terminal and it performs the logical function

$$F = A\overline{B} + \overline{A}B = A \oplus B \tag{2.10}$$

The truth table describing this function is given by Table 2.15. The output F of the gate is at logic 1 only when either one, but not both,

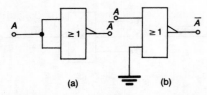

Fig. 2.16 The NOR gate connected as an inverter

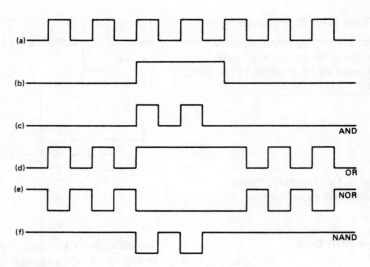

Fig. 2.17

Table 2.15 Exclusive-OR gate

A	0	1	0	1
B	0	0	1	1
F	0	1	1	0

The Exclusive-NOR Gate

of its inputs is also at logic 1. If both inputs are at logic 0 or at logic 1, the output of the gate will be at 0.

The exclusive-OR gate can be fabricated by suitably combining other types of gate and it can also be obtained in an integrated circuit package. Figure 2.18 shows how an exclusive-OR gate can be made using a mixture of AND, OR and NOR gates.

The coincidence, or exclusive-NOR, gate is one which has two input terminals and one output terminal. It produces the logical 1 state at the output only when the two inputs are at the same logical state. The truth table of a coincidence gate is given by Table 2.16.

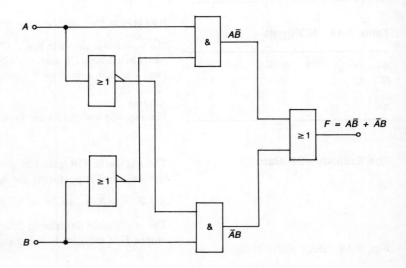

Fig. 2.18 Exclusive-OR gate

Table 2.16 Coincidence gate

A	0	1	0	1
B	0	0	1	1
F	1	0	0	1

From the truth table it is apparent that the Boolean equation describing a coincidence gate is

$$F = \overline{A}\overline{B} + AB \qquad (2.11)$$

If equation (2.11) is inverted

$$\overline{F} = \overline{\overline{A}\overline{B} + AB}$$
$$= \overline{\overline{A}\overline{B}} \cdot \overline{AB}$$
$$= (A + B)(\overline{A} + \overline{B})$$
$$= A\overline{A} + A\overline{B} + B\overline{A} + B\overline{B}$$
$$= A\overline{B} + \overline{A}B$$

(using DeMorgan's rules, page 19).

which is the equation for an exclusive-OR gate. Hence a coincidence gate performs the inverse function to an exclusive-OR gate.

Applications of Logic Gates

The number of possible applications of logic gates is extremely large and in this section of the chapter some simple examples are given.

Door Alarm

A system is required which will allow a door to be opened only when the correct combination of four push-buttons is pressed. Any incorrect combination is required to bring up an alarm.

Let the four buttons be labelled as A, B, C and D and suppose that the correct combination to open the door is $A = 1$, $B = 1$, $C = 0$ and $D = 0$. Then the output F of the system which opens the door is

$$F = AB\overline{C}\overline{D}$$

and the system can be implemented using a 4-input AND gate and two NOT gates as shown by Fig. 2.19. The alarm requirement is easily

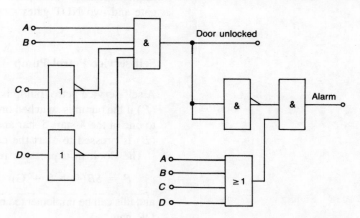

Fig. 2.19 Door alarm circuit

satisfied by connecting the output of the 4-input AND gate via a NOT gate to the alarm circuit. Further circuitry would be needed to ensure that the alarm did not operate continually, and hence the NOT gate output is fed into an AND gate along with the output of an OR gate whose inputs are the four push-buttons. The alarm will now operate only when A or B or C or D and the output of the NAND gate are at 1.

High-Voltage Power Supply

Access (A) to the high-voltage section of a radio transmitter should only be possible if (i) the power (P) has been switched off, (ii) the door to the section has been unlocked with a special key (D) to ensure that the power cannot be turned on again by another person, (iii) the h.t. line (H) has been earthed.

The Boolean expression describing this action is

$$A = \bar{P}DH$$

and this is easily implemented using one 3-input AND gate and one NOT gate.

Motor Control

An electrical motor is to operate when (i) the power supply is connected (P), (ii) the current taken from the supply is less than some safety factor figure (I), (iii) the power supply should not be able to be switched on unless a safety guard (S) is in position, although this can be overridden by a maintenance technician by means of a special key (K).

The required logical function is

$$F = PIS\bar{K} + PI\bar{S}K$$

Implementation will require two 4-input AND gates, one 2-input OR gate and two NOT gates.

Self-service Petrol Pump

A self-service petrol pump is to provide the required grade of petrol (P) if the pump is switched on (S), and the grade selector is positioned to one of the 4-star, 5-star and green positions (4, 5, G) and a button (B) is pressed to alert the cashier that the pump is in operation.

The Boolean expression representing this action is

$$P = SB(4 + 5 + G)$$

and this can be implemented by one 3-input AND gate and one 3-input OR gate.

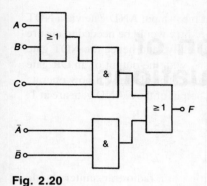

Fig. 2.20

Deducing the Truth Table of a Given Circuit

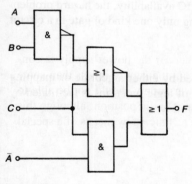

Fig. 2.21

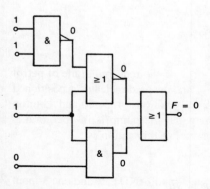

Fig. 2.22

Machine Control

An electrically controlled machine should only operate (O) if the power supply is switched on (P), a safety guard is in place (G), either manual (M) or automatic (A) operation has been selected, and, lastly, fast, medium or slow speed has been chosen (F or N or S).

The logical operation of the machine is

$$O = PG(M + A)(F + N + S)$$

Implementation requires one 2-input OR gate, one 3-input OR gate, and one 4-input AND gate.

Sometimes it is necessary to be able to determine the truth table of a given combinational logic circuit. Consider the circuit shown in Fig. 2.20. Starting from the inputs to the circuit the Boolean equation for the output of each gate should be written down until eventually the expression for the output F of the circuit is obtained.

Thus, referring to Fig. 2.20. The output of the input OR gate is $A + B$ and the outputs of the two AND gates are (top) $(A + B)C$ and (bottom) $\bar{A}\bar{B}$. Then the output F of the circuit is $F = (A + B)C + \bar{A}\bar{B}$. The truth table of the circuit is shown by Table 2.17.

Table 2.17

A	B	C	$A + B$	$(A + AB)C$	$\bar{A}$	$\bar{B}$	$\bar{A}\bar{B}$	F
0	0	0	0	0	1	1	1	1
1	0	0	1	0	0	1	0	0
0	1	0	1	0	1	0	0	0
1	1	0	1	0	0	0	0	0
0	0	1	0	0	1	1	1	1
1	0	1	1	1	0	1	0	1
0	1	1	1	1	1	0	0	1
1	1	1	1	1	0	0	0	1

The truth table can be employed to determine the output of the circuit for any particular combination of the input variables. For example, if $A = B = C = 1$ then the output F is 1. If the requirement is merely to find the output of a circuit for a particular set of input variables it is not necessary to first obtain the truth table. The logic state of each input can be marked on the circuit and the state of each gate output found until the output F is determined.

EXAMPLE 2.7

The circuit of Fig. 2.21 has inputs $A = B = C = 1$. Find the output state of the circuit.

Solution
See Fig. 2.22.

3 Simplification of Boolean Equations

When a combinational or random logic circuit is to be designed to solve a logic problem a Boolean equation and/or a truth table describing the required circuit operation may be produced. Very often the equation first obtained is not in its minimal form and it can then be simplified or *reduced*. If it is possible to reduce a Boolean equation to a simpler form fewer gates will be needed to implement the design. Usually this will mean that fewer integrated circuits (ICs) are employed with a consequent reduction in both costs and in physical dimensions. There are, however, some other factors that also have to be kept in mind; these include the question of IC availability, the hazard problem (p. 36), and the desirability of using only one kind of gate in a circuit (p. 22).

Algebraic Method

Boolean equations can be simplified by either algebraic or mapping methods. Algebraic simplification of logic functions is facilitated by the use of the **logic rules** which follow.

$$1 \quad A + \bar{A} = 1$$
$$2 \quad A + A = A$$
$$3 \quad AA = A$$
$$4 \quad A\bar{A} = 0$$
$$5 \quad A(B + C) = AB + AC$$
$$6 \quad A + 0 = A$$
$$7 \quad A + 1 = 1$$
$$8 \quad A1 = A$$
$$9 \quad A0 = 0$$
$$10 \quad AB = BA$$
$$11 \quad A + B = B + A$$
$$12 \quad B(A + \bar{A}) = B$$
$$13 \quad A + AB = A$$
$$14 \quad A(A + B) = A$$
$$15 \quad A + \bar{A}B = A + B$$
$$16 \quad A(\bar{A} + B) = AB$$
$$17 \quad \overline{A + B} = \bar{A}\bar{B}$$
$$18 \quad \overline{AB} = \bar{A} + \bar{B}$$
$$19 \quad AB + \bar{B}C + AC = AB + \bar{B}C$$

Table 3.1 De Morgan's first rule

A	B	A + B	$\overline{A + B}$	$\overline{A}$	$\overline{B}$	$\overline{A}\,\overline{B}$
0	0	0	1	1	1	1
1	0	1	0	0	1	0
0	1	1	0	1	0	0
1	1	1	0	0	0	0

Table 3.2 De Morgan's second rule

A	B	AB	$\overline{AB}$	$\overline{A}$	$\overline{B}$	$\overline{A} + \overline{B}$
0	0	0	1	1	1	1
1	0	0	1	0	1	1
0	1	0	1	1	0	1
1	1	1	0	0	0	0

All of these rules can easily be confirmed by the use of basic logic (i.e. $1 + 0 = 1$, $1.0 = 0$), or a truth table, as will now be shown for some rules. Rules 17 and 18 are known as **De Morgan's rules** and are particularly useful. The truth table for rule 17 is given in Table 3.1. Obviously, the fourth and the last columns are identical so that, for all values of A and B,

$$\overline{A + B} = \overline{A}\,\overline{B}$$

Table 3.2 gives the truth table for the De Morgan's second rule, i.e. rule 18. Again, the fourth and last columns are identical and the rule is confirmed.

De Morgan's rules can be stated in the following manner. The complement of a function F can be obtained by, first, replacing each variable by its complement and then interchanging all AND ($\cdot$) and OR ($+$) signs.

Both of De Morgan's rules can be extended to deal with three, or more, input variables. Thus

$$F = \overline{A + B + C} = \overline{A}\,\overline{B}\,\overline{C} \qquad \text{(rule 17)}$$
$$F = \overline{ABC} = \overline{A} + \overline{B} + \overline{C} \qquad \text{(rule 18)}$$

EXAMPLE 3.1

If $F = A\overline{B} + C$ find $\overline{F}$.

Solution
Using rule 17, $\overline{F} = \overline{A\overline{B}} \cdot \overline{C}$
Using rule 18, $\overline{F} = (\overline{A} + B)\overline{C} = \overline{A}\overline{C} + B\overline{C}$

EXAMPLE 3.2

Simplify $F = \overline{(A + B)(\overline{A} + C)}$

Solution

$$F = \overline{\overline{A + B} + \overline{\overline{A} + C}} \qquad \text{(rule 18)}$$
$$= \overline{A}\overline{B} + A\overline{C} \qquad \text{(rule 17)}$$

The accuracy of the other rules can also be confirmed. For example:

Rule 1   If $A = 1$ then $\overline{A} = 0$: hence $1 + 0 = 1$
          If $A = 0$ then $\overline{A} = 1$: hence $0 + 1 = 1$
Rule 7   If $A = 1$ then $1 + 1 = 1$, if $A = 0$ then $1 + 0 = 1$
Rule 14 If $A = 1$ then $1(1 + B) = 1 \cdot 1 + 1 \cdot B = 1 + B = 1$
          If $A = 0$ then $0(0 + B) = 0 + 0 \cdot B = 0$
Rule 15 The truth table is given by Table 3.3
Rule 19 Table 3.4 gives the truth table for this rule

Table 3.3

A	B	$\overline{A}$	$\overline{A}B$	$A + \overline{A}B$	$A + B$
0	0	1	0	0	0
1	0	0	0	1	1
0	1	1	1	1	1
1	1	0	0	1	1

Table 3.4

A	B	C	$\overline{B}$	AB	$\overline{B}C$	AC	$AB + \overline{B}C + AC$	$AB + \overline{B}C$
0	0	0	1	0	0	0	0	0
1	0	0	1	0	0	0	0	0
0	1	0	0	0	0	0	0	0
1	1	0	0	1	0	0	1	1
0	0	1	1	0	1	0	1	1
1	0	1	1	0	1	1	1	1
0	1	1	0	0	0	0	0	0
1	1	1	0	1	0	1	1	1

Rule 19 is, perhaps, rather difficult to remember and to apply but it can be very useful. It applies whenever there is the product of two input variables (AB) and the product of the complement of one of these variables and a third input variable ($\overline{B}C$). If the product of the non-complemented input variable (A) and the third variable (C) exists then the term AC is redundant.

It is necessary to be able to express the output of a logical network in terms of Boolean algebra and also, given the Boolean expression for a required output, to be able to design the logic circuitry needed to produce this output. When designing a logic network, the required function is generally first simplified, using the rules 1–19, in an effort to minimize the number of gates required, although it must be noted that the simplest Boolean expression does not necessarily give the minimum number of gates.

EXAMPLE 3.3

Draw the logic circuit that will implement the Boolean expression $F = (A + B)(B + C)$. Also, simplify the expression and draw the circuit that will implement the simplified equation.

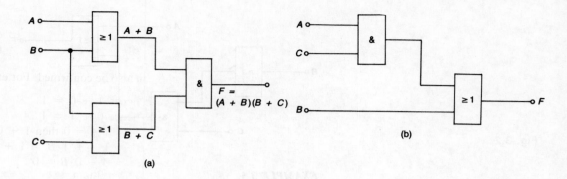

Fig. 3.1

Solution

$$F = (A + B)(B + C)$$
$$= AB + AC + BB + BC$$
$$= AB + AC + B + BC \quad \text{rule 3}$$
$$= AB + AC + B(1 + C)$$
$$= A(B + C) + B \quad \text{rule 7}$$
$$= AC + B(1 + A)$$
$$= AC + B \quad \text{rule 7}$$

Figures 3.1 *a* and *b* show, respectively, the logical circuitry required to implement the equation $F = (A + B)(B + C)$ and its simplified version $F = AC + B$. Clearly the saving in the number of gates needed is small, the number being reduced from three to two. If integrated circuit gates (see Chapter 3) are used, there might be no saving at all since a single integrated circuit package will contain four 2-input AND or OR gates.

EXAMPLE 3.4

Simplify the Boolean equation

$$F = \overline{\overline{A}(B + \overline{C})}(A + \overline{B} + C)(\overline{\overline{A}\overline{B}\overline{C}})$$

and draw the circuit which will implement the simplified equation.

Solution

$$F = (A + \overline{B} + \overline{C})(A + \overline{B} + C)(A + B + C)$$
$$= (A + \overline{B}C)(AA + AB + AC + A\overline{B} + \overline{B}B + \overline{B}C +$$
$$\quad AC + BC + CC)$$
$$= (A + \overline{B}C)[A + A(B + C) + \overline{B}(A + C) + C(B + A) + C]$$
$$= (A + \overline{B}C)[A(1 + B + C) + \overline{B}(A + C) + C(1 + B + A)]$$
$$= (A + \overline{B}C)[A + \overline{B}A + \overline{B}C + C]$$
$$= (A + \overline{B}C)[A(1 + \overline{B}) + C(1 + \overline{B})]$$
$$= (A + \overline{B}C)(A + C)$$
$$= AA + AC + A\overline{B}C + \overline{B}C$$
$$= A(1 + C) + \overline{B}C(1 + A)$$
$$= A + \overline{B}C$$

Figure 3.2 shows the required circuit.

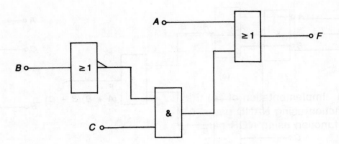

Fig. 3.2

EXAMPLE 3.5

Confirm rule 19, i.e. $AB + \bar{B}C + AC = AB + \bar{B}C$.

Solution

$$\begin{aligned}
AB + \bar{B}C &= AB(1 + C) + \bar{B}C(1 + A) \qquad\qquad \text{rule 7}\\
&= AB + ABC + \bar{B}C + A\bar{B}C\\
&= AB + \bar{B}C + AC(B + \bar{B})\\
&= AB + \bar{B}C + AC \qquad\qquad\qquad\qquad \text{rule 1}
\end{aligned}$$

EXAMPLE 3.6

Simplify $F = \overline{A(B + C)} + \bar{A}B + \bar{C}\overline{(A + B)}$

Solution

$$\begin{aligned}
F &= \bar{A} + \overline{B + C} + \bar{A}B + \bar{C}(\bar{A}\bar{B}) \qquad \text{rules 17 and 18}\\
&= \bar{A} + \bar{B}\bar{C} + \bar{A}B + \bar{A}\bar{B}\bar{C} \qquad\qquad \text{rule 17}\\
&= \bar{A}(1 + B) + \bar{B}\bar{C}(1 + \bar{A})\\
&= \bar{A} + \bar{B}\bar{C} \qquad\qquad\qquad\qquad\qquad \text{rule 7}
\end{aligned}$$

EXAMPLE 3.7

Simplify $F = \bar{A}(\bar{B} + \bar{C}) + BC + A\bar{C}$

Solution

$$\begin{aligned}
F &= \bar{A}\bar{B} + \bar{A}\bar{C} + BC + A\bar{C}\\
&= \bar{A}\bar{B} + \bar{C}(A + \bar{A}) + BC \qquad\qquad \text{rule 1}\\
&= \bar{A}\bar{B} + B + \bar{C} \qquad\qquad\qquad\qquad \text{rule 15}\\
&= \bar{A} + B + \bar{C} \qquad\qquad\qquad\qquad\quad \text{rule 15}
\end{aligned}$$

The Use of NAND/NOR Gates to Generate AND/OR Functions

The majority of integrated circuit gates employed in modern equipment belong to one or other of two logic families, namely the **TTL** and the **CMOS** families. In both of these families, NAND and NOR gates are the most commonly used since their cost is less than that of the other types of gate which are available. Also, the NAND and NOR gates generally have a faster operating speed and a lower power dissipation. Very often, therefore, a random logic circuit is made up using *only* NAND and/or NOR gates.

It is easy to see that the AND function can be obtained by **cascading**

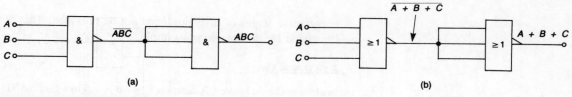

Fig. 3.3 Implementation of (*a*) the AND function using NAND gates, (*b*) the OR function using NOR gates

two NAND gates as shown by Fig. 3.3*a*, the second gate being employed as an inverter. Similarly, the OR function is easily obtained by the cascade connection of two NOR gates (Fig. 3.3*b*).

Implementation of the AND function using NOR gates, and of the OR function using NAND gates, is not quite as easy but the necessary connections can readily be deduced by the use of De Morgan's rules. Rule 18 is

$$\overline{AB} = \overline{A} + \overline{B}$$

hence

$$AB = \overline{\overline{A} + \overline{B}}$$

The right-hand expression is easily implemented using NOR gates as shown in Fig. 3.4*a*.

The other De Morgan rule is

$$\overline{A + B} = \overline{A}\,\overline{B}$$

hence

$$A + B = \overline{\overline{A}\,\overline{B}}$$

and this expression can be implemented using NAND gates as shown in Fig. 3.4*b*.

Clearly, more gates are needed to implement the AND/OR functions with NAND/NOR gates, but very often the apparent increase in the number of gates required is not as great as at first anticipated since

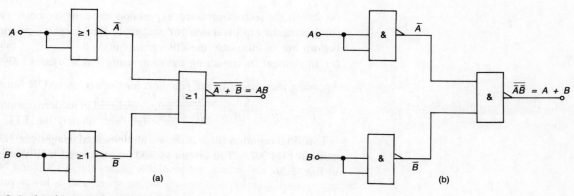

Fig. 3.4 Implementation of (*a*) the AND function using NOR gates, (*b*) the OR function using NAND gates

consecutive stages of inversion need not be provided. This point is illustrated by the following example.

EXAMPLE 3.8

Implement the exclusive-OR function $F = A\bar{B} + \bar{A}B$ using (i) NAND gates only, (ii) NOR gates only.

Solution
The first step is to draw the logic diagram using AND, OR and NOT gates. When this has been done, replace each gate with its (i) NAND, (ii) NOR equivalent circuit. Finally, if possible simplify the resulting network by eliminating any redundant gates.

(i) Figure 2.18 shows the exclusive-OR gate built with AND and OR gates. Replacing each gate with the equivalent NAND logic network gives the circuit of Fig. 3.5a. It can be seen that this network includes two sets of two NAND gates in cascade. These are redundant since $\bar{\bar{A}} = A$. Figure 3.5b shows the simplified network which does not include the four redundant gates. It will be noticed that the number of NAND gates required (i.e. 5) to implement the exclusive-OR gate is the same as the number of AND and OR gates which are necessary.

(ii) Replacing each AND and each OR gate with the corresponding NOR gate version results in the circuit of Fig. 3.6a and this can be simplified by eliminating redundant gates to produce the final version given in Fig. 3.6b.

In general, Boolean equations in the *product-of-sums* form, e.g. $(A + B)(C + D)$, are best implemented using NOR gates, and *sum-of-product* equations, e.g. $AB + CD$, are more easily implemented using NAND gates.

The NAND and NOR circuits can be obtained directly from the Boolean equations by employing the technique of 'double inversion'.

NAND Gate

(a) Invert the sum-of-products expression to be implemented twice.
(b) Retain the top inversion bar and apply De Morgan's rule to the bottom bar to eliminate the OR operation(s).
(c) Implement the resulting equation using NAND gates only.

Applying these steps to the equation for the exclusive OR function:

$$F = A\bar{B} + \bar{A}B = \overline{\overline{A\bar{B} + \bar{A}B}} = \overline{\overline{A\bar{B}}.\overline{\bar{A}B}}$$

This final equation for F is shown implemented using three NAND gates in Fig. 3.7a. The circuit should be compared with that given in Fig. 3.5b.

NOR Gate

(a) Invert the product-of-sums equation to be implemented twice.

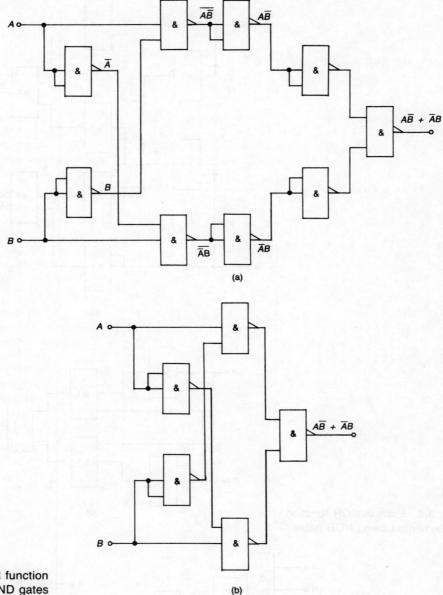

Fig. 3.5 Exclusive-OR function
implemented using NAND gates

(b) Retain the upper inversion bar and apply De Morgan's other rule
to the lower bar to remove the AND operation(s).
(c) Implement the resulting equation using NOR gates only.

In product-of-sums form the equation for the exclusive OR function is:

$$F = A\bar{B} + \bar{A}B = (A + B)(\bar{A} + \bar{B}) = \overline{\overline{(A + B)(\bar{A} + \bar{B})}}$$
$$= \overline{\overline{(A + B)} + \overline{(\bar{A} + \bar{B})}}$$

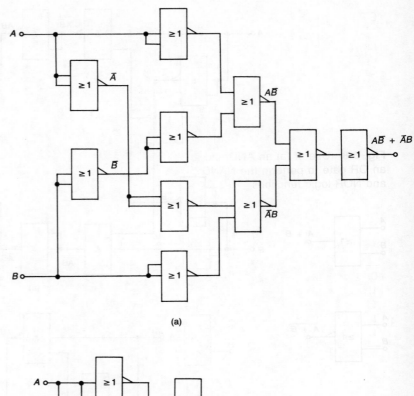

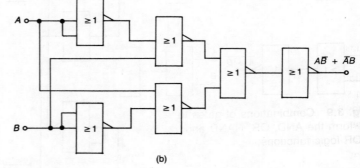

Fig. 3.6 Exclusive-OR function implemented using NOR gates

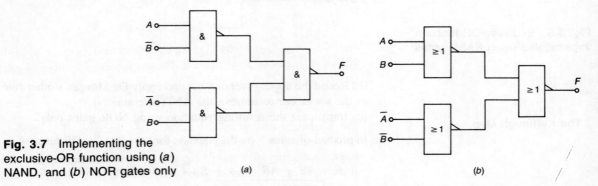

Fig. 3.7 Implementing the exclusive-OR function using (a) NAND, and (b) NOR gates only

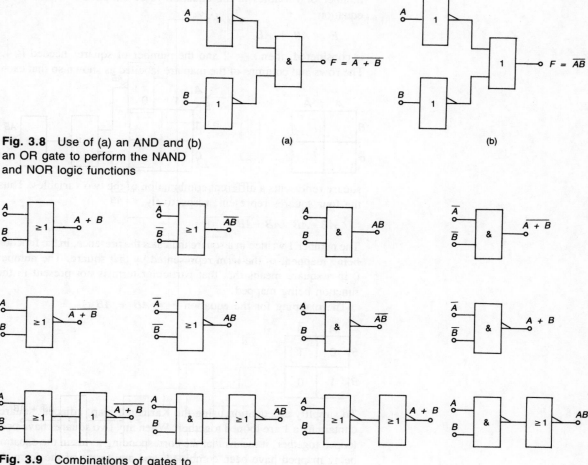

Fig. 3.8 Use of (a) an AND and (b) an OR gate to perform the NAND and NOR logic functions

(a)

(b)

Fig. 3.9 Combinations of gates to perform the AND, OR, NAND and NOR logic functions

This equation for F is shown implemented, using three NOR gates, in Fig. 3.7b. This circuit should be compared with Fig. 3.6b.

If an AND gate is preceded by a NOT gate, Fig. 3.8a, its output F is

$$F = \overline{A}\overline{B} = \overline{A + B}, \text{ the NOR function.}$$

Similarly, if an OR gate is fed with complemented inputs, Fig. 3.8b, the NAND function is performed. The various combinations of gates are summarized by Fig. 3.9.

The Karnaugh Map

The Karnaugh map provides a convenient method of simplifying Boolean equations in which the function to be simplified is displayed diagrammatically on a set of squares. Each square maps one term of the function. The number of squares is equal to 2^n, where n is the number of variables in the equation to be simplified. Thus, if the equation

$$F = A\bar{B} + \bar{A}B$$

is considered, then $n = 2$ and the number of squares needed is 4. The rows and columns of the map are labelled as shown so that each

square represents a different combination of the two variables. Thus the four squares represent, respectively,

$$AB \quad \bar{A}B \quad A\bar{B} \quad \bar{A}\bar{B}$$

The number 1 written in a square indicates the presence, in the function being mapped, of the term represented by that square. The number 0 in a square means that that particular term is not present in the function being mapped.

The mapping for the equation $F = A\bar{B} + \bar{A}B$ is

	A	Ā
B	0	1
B̄	1	0

To simplify an equation using the Karnaugh map, adjacent squares containing a 1 are looped together. When any two squares have been looped together, it means that the corresponding terms in the equation being mapped have been combined; and any terms of the form $A\bar{A}$ have been eliminated.

For example consider the equation $F = AB + \bar{A}B + A\bar{B}$

	A	Ā
B	1	1
B̄	0	1

Looping adjacent squares in the map as shown

	A	Ā
B	1	1
B̄	0	1

simplifies the equation to

$$F = \bar{A}(B + \bar{B}) + B(A + \bar{A}) = \bar{A} + B$$

The Karnaugh map is easily extended for use with three variables A, B and C as shown by the following examples, or with four variables A, B, C and D. Squares must only be looped together in multiples of two, i.e. in twos, in fours, or in eights.

EXAMPLE 3.9

Use a Karnaugh map to simplify the equation

$$F = AC + \bar{A}BC + \bar{B}C$$

Solution
The Karnaugh map of the equation is

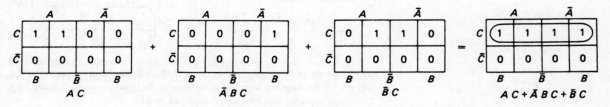

Normally, of course, the complete mapping would be written down directly. Looping the four adjacent squares simplifies the equation to

$$F = C$$

EXAMPLE 3.10

Use a Karnaugh map to simplify the Boolean expression

$$F = ABC + \bar{A}\bar{B}\bar{C} + AB\bar{C} + \bar{A}\bar{C}$$

Solution
The mapping of the expression is

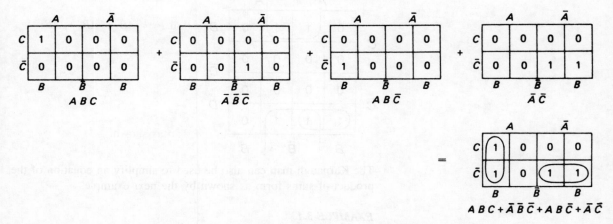

The squares can be looped together in two groups of two as shown.
From this mapping,

$$F = AB + \bar{A}\bar{C}$$

EXAMPLE 3.11

Simplify the Boolean equation $F = ACD + AB\bar{C}D + \bar{A}BD + A\bar{B}\bar{C}D$.

Solution

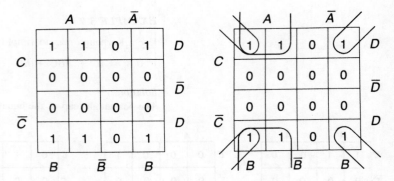

The mapping of the expression is given in the left-hand map. Squares in the top row of the map are adjacent to squares in the bottom row so that the left-hand four squares can be looped together to give AD.

The four corner squares can also be looped together to give BD. Hence, the simplified equation is $F = AD + BD$.

EXAMPLE 3.12

Map, and then simplify, $F = \bar{A}\bar{B}\bar{C}D + AB\bar{C}D + A\bar{B}\bar{C}D + \bar{A}BCD + A\bar{B}CD$.

Solution
From the map,

$$F = \bar{B}D + A\bar{C}D$$

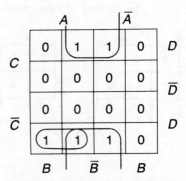

The Karnaugh map can also be used to simplify an equation of the product-of-sums form as shown by the next example.

EXAMPLE 3.13

Use a Karnaugh map to simplify the equation

$$F = (AC + A\bar{C}D)(AD + AC + BC)$$

Solution

The mappings of $(AC + A\bar{C}D)$ and $(AD + AC + BC)$ are

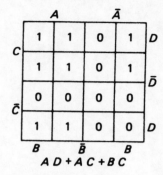

To combine the two maps to obtain the mapping of F, note that $1.1 = 1$ and $1.0 = 0$. Hence ANDing the two maps gives

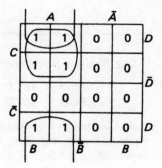

Hence

$$F = AC + AD$$

To check, using the logic rules given on page 18, first multiply out the equation to give

$$F = ACAD + ACAC + ACBC + A\bar{C}DAD + \\ A\bar{C}DAC + A\bar{C}DBC$$

But $AA = A \quad CC = C \quad \bar{C}C = 0$ and so

$$F = ACD + AC + ABC + A\bar{C}D \\ = AD(C + \bar{C}) + AC(1 + B) \\ = AD + AC$$

When a Boolean equation has been mapped on a Karnaugh map the inverse of the function can easily be obtained by looping the squares that contain a 0. Referring:

A To Example 3.9: looping the 0 squares gives $\bar{F} = \bar{C}$

B To Example 3.10: $\bar{F} = \bar{A}C + A\bar{B}$

C To Example 3.11: $\bar{F} = \bar{D} + \bar{A}B$

D To Example 3.12: $\bar{F} = \bar{D} + \bar{A}B + BC$

Designing a Circuit from a Truth Table

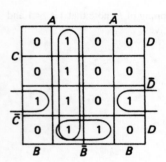

If the truth table of a required logical operation is written down, it can be used to derive an expression for the output signal of the necessary circuit. This, after suitable simplification, can be implemented by the interconnection of a number of appropriate gates. Each 1 appearing in the output column of the truth table must be represented by a term in the Boolean equation describing the circuit. This term must contain each input variable that is at 1 and the complement of each variable that is at 0.

As an example of the technique consider the truth table given by Table 3.5.

Table 3.5

A	0	0	0	0	0	0	0	1	1	1	1	1	1	1	1
B	0	0	0	1	1	1	1	0	0	0	0	1	1	1	1
C	0	0	1	0	0	1	1	0	0	1	1	0	0	1	1
D	0	1	0	1	0	1	0	1	0	1	0	1	0	1	0
F	0	1	0	0	1	0	0	1	1	1	1	0	1	0	0

The Boolean expression for this circuit is

$$F = \bar{A}\bar{B}\bar{C}D + \bar{A}B\bar{C}\bar{D} + A\bar{B}\bar{C}D + A\bar{B}\bar{C}\bar{D} + A\bar{B}C\bar{D} + \\ A\bar{B}CD + ABC\bar{D}$$

The Karnaugh mapping of the function F is shown with adjacent squares looped together. From the map the simplified equation representing the logical operation given by the truth table is

$$F = A\bar{B} + \bar{B}C\bar{D} + \bar{B}CD$$

If a product-of-sums equation for the output signal is required each 0 appearing in the output column of the truth table must be represented by a term in the Boolean equation describing the circuit. This term must contain each input variable that is at 0 and the complement of each input variable that is at 1.

Consider the truth table of a circuit that is given in Table 3.6. The sum-of-products expression for the circuit is

$$F = \bar{A}\bar{B}\bar{C} + \bar{A}\bar{B}C + \bar{A}BC + ABC$$

The product-of-sums expression is

$$F = (\bar{A} + B + C)(A + \bar{B} + C)(\bar{A} + \bar{B} + C)(\bar{A} + B + \bar{C})$$

[Both equations reduce to $F = \bar{A}\bar{B} + BC$.]

Another example is the design of a **half-adder**; this is a circuit that adds two inputs A and B to produce a SUM and a CARRY but cannot take account of any carry originating from a previous stage. The truth table of a half-adder is given by Table 3.7.

From the truth table the sum and the carry of A and B are

$$S = A\bar{B} + \bar{A}B \qquad C = AB$$

Table 3.6

A	0	1	0	1	0	1	0	1
B	0	0	1	1	0	0	1	1
C	0	0	0	0	1	1	1	1
F	1	0	0	0	1	0	1	1

Table 3.7 Half-adder

A	0	1	0	1
B	0	0	1	1
Sum	0	1	1	0
Carry	0	0	0	1

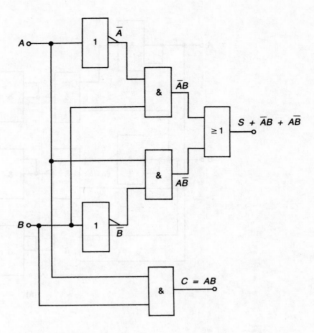

Fig. 3.10   Half-adder circuit

Implementing these equations using AND, NOT, and OR gates gives the logic circuit shown in Fig. 3.10.

The first step in obtaining the NAND version of this circuit is to replace each AND and each OR gate by its NAND equivalent. This has been done for the Fig. 3.10 circuit and the result is given in Fig. 3.11a. The circuit can then be simplified by the removal of redundant gates to give the circuit of Fig. 3.11b. Similarly, the NOR gate version of the 3.10 circuit is shown by Fig. 3.11c. It can be seen that in this case there are four redundant gates. Removing these gives Fig. 3.11d.

Comparing the half-adder circuits shown in Figs 3.11b and d, it is clear that the NOR version requires two more gates than the NAND equivalent. This is an indication that the NAND gate implementation of logical functions is more suited to those functions in sum-of-products form. Conversely, NOR gate implementation is the most appropriate for a function in product-of-sums form.

It might appear that the NAND/NOR circuits will require more ICs than the circuit of Fig. 3.10. This, however, is not the case. Figure 3.10 uses two NOT, three AND and one OR gate which would require *three* ICs. Figure 3.11b uses seven NAND gates and Fig. 3.11d uses nine NOR gates; these are provided by just *two* or *three* ICs.

Don't Care/Can't Happen States

In some logical circuits certain combinations of the input variables **can't happen**. Hence, when writing down the truth table of the circuit

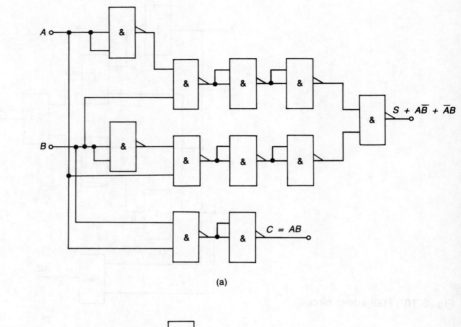

(a)

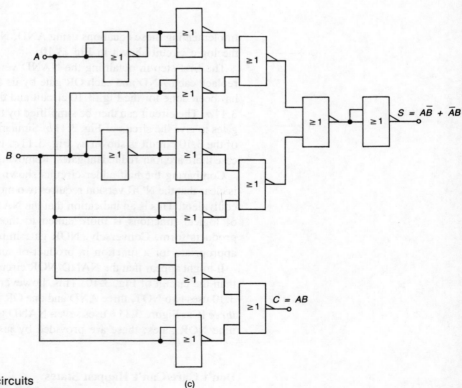

(c)

Fig. 3.11 Half-adder circuits
implemented with (*a*) and (*b*) NAND
gates only, (*c*) and (*d*) NOR gates
only

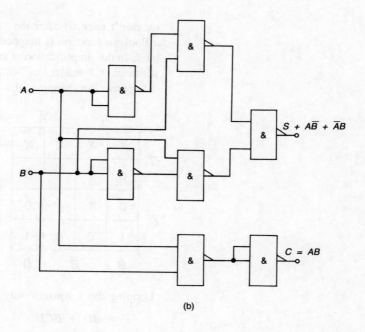

(b)

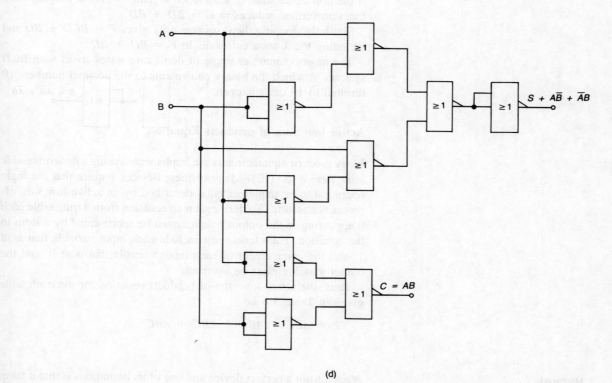

(d)

we **don't care** whether the variables are listed as 1 or as 0. When a Boolean function is mapped any don't care terms are represented by X. In the simplification of an expression an X square may be looped with *either* 1 squares *or* with 0 squares.

Suppose the mapping of a function is:

	A		$\bar{A}$		
	X	X	X	X	D
C					
	0	1	1	0	$\bar{D}$
	0	1	1	0	
$\bar{C}$					D
	1	0	0	1	
	B	$\bar{B}$	B		

Looping the 1 squares only gives

$$F = \bar{B}\bar{D} + B\bar{C}D$$

If the don't care squares are looped together with the 1 squares the function further reduces to $F = \bar{B}\bar{D} + BD$.

Similarly, looping the 0 squares only gives $\bar{F} = \bar{B}\bar{C}D + B\bar{D}$ and including the X squares results in $\bar{F} = B\bar{D} + \bar{B}D$.

The most common example of don't care states arises with BCD systems in which the binary equivalents to the decimal numbers 10 through to 15 can't happen.

Active-low Sum-of-products Equation

Many modern digital circuits are implemented using a *programmable logic device* (p. 103). Many of these devices require that the logic operation to be implemented is described by an active-low sum-of-products equation. To derive such an equation from a truth table each 0 appearing in the output column must be represented by a term in the equation. Each term must include each input variable that is at 1, and the complement of each input variable that is at 0, and the output variable must be inverted.

Thus, the active-low sum-of-products equation for the truth table given in Table 3.6 is

$$\bar{F} = A\bar{B}\bar{C} + \bar{A}B\bar{C} + AB\bar{C} + A\bar{B}C$$

Hazards

A gate is not a perfect device and one of its limitations is that it takes a short, yet finite, time to operate. The delay produced may be only

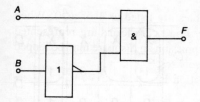

Fig. 3.12 Circuit with a static hazard

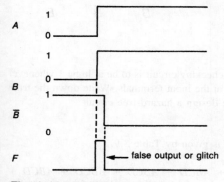

Fig. 3.13 Waveforms for Fig. 3.12

Table 3.8

Denary	Input Binary				Output
	D	C	B	A	
0	0	0	0	0	0
1	0	0	0	1	0
2	0	0	1	0	1
3	0	0	1	1	0
4	0	1	0	0	0
5	0	1	0	1	1
6	0	1	1	0	1
7	0	1	1	1	1
8	1	0	0	0	0
9	1	0	0	1	0

a few milliseconds but it may lead to errors in the output signal of a combinational logic circuit.

A *static hazard* exists in a combinational logic circuit when a change in a single input variable causes a transient change, or glitch, at the output when no such change should have taken place. The Boolean expression representing Fig. 3.12 is $F = A\bar{B}$. When $A = B = 0$ the output of the circuit will be 0. If, now, A and B change simultaneously to 1 the output of the circuit should remain at 0. However, because of the time delay introduced by the inverting stage the output will momentarily go to 1. The waveforms for the circuit are shown in Fig. 3.13. A hazard is always likely if adjacent 1 squares in a Karnaugh mapping are not looped together. The hazard can be removed by ensuring that all adjacent 1 squares *are* looped together. This will generally mean that the minimal solution to a mapped equation is not obtained.

Consider the equation $F = AC + B\bar{C}$. When $A = B = 1$, F should be of the form $C + \bar{C} = 1$. If C changes from 1 to 0, $\bar{C}$ will − after a short time delay − change from 0 to 1. For a short time, therefore, both C and $\bar{C}$ will be at the logical 0 state and the output of the circuit will be incorrect.

The mapping of $F = AC + B\bar{C}$ is

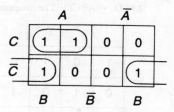

The static hazard can be eliminated by looping the ABC and $AB\bar{C}$ squares as well to give the term AB. Now $F = AB + B\bar{C} + AC$ and the output will be at logic 1 when $A = B = 1$ regardless of the state of C (and $\bar{C}$).

EXAMPLE 3.14

Design a combinational logic circuit that has 10 inputs, numbered 0 through to 9, and one output. The output is required to go high whenever any one, or more, of the inputs numbered 2, 5, 6 or 7 go high. The circuit should either employ NAND gates, or NOR gates only, and be free of static hazards.

Solution
The truth table for the required circuit is given by Table 3.8.

From the truth table the Boolean equation describing the circuit is $F = \bar{A}BC\bar{D} + A\bar{B}C\bar{D} + \bar{A}\bar{B}C\bar{D} + ABC\bar{D}$. This equation is mapped as shown. If the 1 squares are looped to minimize the equation the result is $F = \bar{A}B + AC$ but a static hazard will exist. To eliminate the hazard a third loop must be introduced to produce the redundant term BC. Hence, $F = \bar{A}B + AC + BC$.

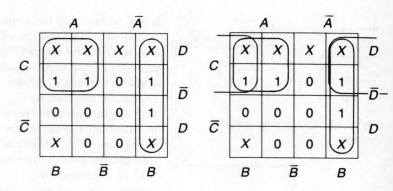

EXAMPLE 3.15

The output of a 4-input parity-checking circuit is to be at logic 1 whenever there is an even number of 1s at the input terminals. Write down the truth table for the circuit and hence design a hazard-free circuit.

Solution
The truth table for the circuit is given by Table 3.9.

From the table $F = AB\bar{C}\bar{D} + A\bar{B}C\bar{D} + \bar{A}BC\bar{D} + A\bar{B}\bar{C}D + \bar{A}B\bar{C}D + \bar{A}\bar{B}CD + ABCD$. The mapping shows that no simplification is possible.

Table 3.9

Inputs				Outputs
D	C	B	A	F
0	0	0	0	0
0	0	0	1	0
0	0	1	0	0
0	0	1	1	1
0	1	0	0	0
0	1	0	1	1
0	1	1	0	1
0	1	1	1	0
1	0	0	0	0
1	0	0	1	1
1	0	1	0	1
1	0	1	1	0
1	1	0	0	1
1	1	0	1	0
1	1	1	0	0
1	1	1	1	1

4 Practical Electronic Gates

The various kinds of electronic gate described in the previous chapter are manufactured in a number of standard types. These are the **transistor-transistor** (TTL), **emitter-coupled logic** (ECL), and **complementary metal oxide semiconductor** (CMOS) logic families. ECL is only used when its special feature, i.e. its very fast speed of operation, is of particular interest. The emphasis throughout this book will be on the TTL and the CMOS logic families.

The advantages to be gained by the use of integrated circuits instead of discrete circuitry are (*a*) a reduction in costs, (*b*) circuits are physically smaller and lighter in weight, (*c*) it is easier to replace a part of a circuit, particularly if IC holders are employed, (*d*) standardization is easier to achieve, and (*e*) power dissipation is much reduced. The main disadvantage is that it may be more difficult to locate faults.

To simplify the manufacture of circuits and later on possibly the location of faults it is preferable for all the ICs used in a particular circuit to be members of the one logic family.

Gates are said to be small-scale integrated circuits (SSI) and a circuit made using a combination of gates is known as a combinational, or random, logic circuit. Random logic still has an important part to play in electronics despite the ever-increasing use of large-scale integration (LSI) and very-large-scale integration (VLSI). Very often there are interfacing, or decoding, tasks that are best performed by a standard SSI chip or a few such circuits.

A small-scale IC has up to 10 devices per chip, a medium-scale IC has between 10 and 100 devices per chip, a large-scale IC has between 100 and 5000 devices per chip, and, lastly, a very-large-scale IC has more than 5000 devices per chip.

Requirements of a Logic Gate

The various families of logic gates possess different characteristics, which mean that one of them may prove to be best suited for a particular application. For example, it may well be that the most important consideration in a particular system is the maximum possible speed of operation; for another system minimum power dissipation might be of overriding importance. The characteristics of the logic families can be classified under the following headings:

(i) Logic levels   (iv) Noise margin or
(ii) Propagation delay   noise immunity
(iii) Fan-in and fan-out   (v) Power dissipation.

Logic Levels

The logic levels of a gate are the input and output voltages that must exist for the circuit to operate correctly. For any practical gate the logic levels are nominally 0 V and $+V_{CC}$ volts but may be anywhere in a range of values above 0 V or below V_{CC} because of voltage drops.

For a TTL gate having a power supply voltage of +5 V the nominal level for binary 1 is +5 V. The minimum input voltage that is guaranteed to be taken as binary 1 is 2 V while the maximum input voltage that can represent binary 0 is 0.8 V. At the output the minimum voltage for binary 1 is 2.4 V and the maximum 0 voltage is 0.4 V. The levels for the other main logic family, the CMOS family, depend upon the supply voltage used.

Propagation Delay

The propagation delay of a logic gate is the time that elapses between the application of a signal to an input terminal and the resulting change in logical state at the output terminal. The delay arises because the output voltage of a switching transistor is unable to change instantaneously from one logic value to another when its input voltage is changed. Suppose the bipolar transistor circuit given in Fig. 4.1a has the rectangular voltage of Fig. 4.1b applied to its base terminal. When the base voltage is zero the transistor is non-conducting or OFF and its collector/emitter voltage V_{CE} is equal to the collector supply voltage V_{CC}. When the base voltage is increased in the positive direc-

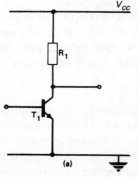
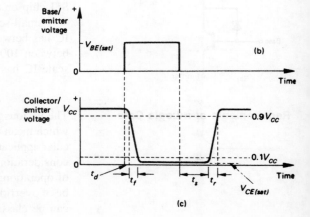

Fig. 4.1 Switching a bipolar transistor circuit: (a) basic circuit, (b) input voltage, (c) output voltage

tion, the transistor starts to conduct current and its collector/emitter voltage falls because of the voltage dropped across the collector load resistor R_L, i.e.

$$V_{CE} = V_{CC} - I_c R_L$$

The collector/emitter voltage does not start to fall at the same instant as the base/emitter voltage goes positive (see Fig. 4.1) but after a time t_d has elapsed.

This time delay is present because of the need for the base current to charge the base/emitter junction capacitance, and because of the time taken for charge carriers to cross the base region. Once the output voltage commences to fall it takes a finite time to do so because the collector/base junction capacitance must also be charged. The **fall-time** t_f is the time taken for the output voltage to fall from 90% to 10% of its OFF value, V_{CC}. When the transistor is fully conducting, or *saturated*, it is said to be ON and then its collector/emitter voltage has fallen to its minimum value, known as the *saturation voltage* $V_{CE(SAT)}$. Once the transistor has saturated, any further increase in the base current cannot produce a further increase in the collector current, since this is limited to $(V_{CC} - V_{CE(SAT)})/R_L$, and the excess charge is stored in the base region of the transistor.

When the base voltage of the transistor is reduced to zero the transistor does not immediately switch OFF; instead there is a time delay t_s before the collector/emitter voltage starts to increase to its OFF value of $+ V_{CC}$ volts. The delay, known as the **storage delay**, is caused by the need for the excess charge stored in the base region to be removed before the collector current can change value. Once the collector/emitter voltage does start to increase, it takes a time, known as the **rise time** t_r, to rise from 10% to 90% of its final (OFF) value. This delay arises from the time taken for the collector current to change between its ON and OFF states.

Usually, t_f and t_r are quite close in value. The propagation delay quoted by the manufacturer is the *average* of these two times.

For standard TTL the total ON and OFF times are about 6 ns and 10 ns respectively and to increase the switching speed the transistor must be prevented from driving into saturation. This can easily be achieved by the connection of a diode between the base and the collector terminals of the transistor as shown by Fig. 4.2. When the transistor is turned ON by a positive voltage applied to its base, its collector/emitter voltage falls and immediately the collector is less positive than the base, diode D_1 conducts and diverts the excess base current away from the base. As a result the transistor does not receive sufficient base current to be driven into saturation and charge storage is no longer a problem. It is best if the diode is of the Schottky type since these devices have zero charge storage and so are very fast switching. A **Schottky transistor** is a bipolar transistor which has a Schottky diode internally connected between its base and collector terminals (Fig. 4.3a). The symbol for a Schottky transistor is given in Fig. 4.3b.

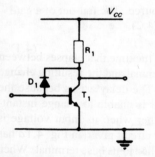

Fig. 4.2 Use of a diode to increase switching speed

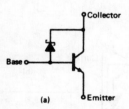

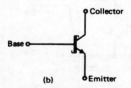

Fig. 4.3 (a) Schottky transistor, (b) symbol

Fan-in and Fan-out

The **fan-in** of a gate is the number of inputs, coming from similar circuits, that can be connected to the gate without adversely affecting its performance. With IC gates it is normally limited by the number of package pins available.

The **fan-out** of a gate is the maximum number of similar circuits that can be connected to its output terminals without the output voltage falling outside the limits at which the logic levels 1 and 0 are specified.

When the output of a driving gate is *low* current will flow into that gate from the driven gate, or gates. The driving gate is then said to be *sinking* current. Conversely, when the output of the driving gate is *high* current flows out of that gate into the driven gate or gates. The driving gate is then said to be *sourcing* current. The two actions are illustrated for TTL gates by Figs 4.4a and b respectively.

When calculating the fan-out of a gate the parameters that are taken into account are the input and output currents for the logic 1 and logic 0 levels. Each gate has a maximum *low* current specification I_{OL} that sets the maximum current that the gate is able to sink. Also, each gate has a maximum *high* current specification I_{OH} that determines the maximum current that the gate may source. The fan-out of a gate is calculated using equations (4.1) and (4.2), i.e.

$$\text{Fan-out (low)} = I_{OL}/I_{IL} \tag{4.1}$$

$$\text{Fan-out (high)} = I_{OH}/I_{IH} \tag{4.2}$$

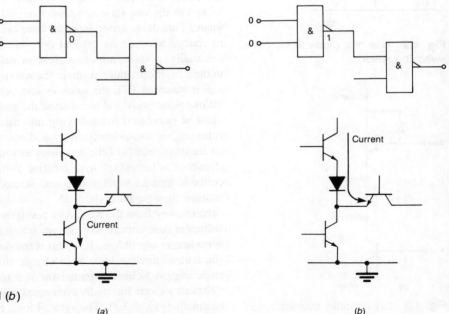

Fig. 4.4 (*a*) Sinking, and (*b*) sourcing, current

(*a*)

(*b*)

where I_{IL} and I_{IH} are respectively the input low, and high, current specifications of the driven gate.

The actual fan-out in any particular case will be the lower of the two figures calculated using these equations.

EXAMPLE 4.1

Calculate the fan-out of a low-power Schottky (LS) TTL gate that is driving other LS TTL gates.

Solution

An LS gate has $I_{IL} = -0.4$ mA, $I_{IH} = 20$ μA, $I_{OL} = 8$ mA, and $I_{OH} = -0.4$ mA.

[The minus signs indicate the direction of current flow and are ignored in the calculation.]

Fan-out (low) = 8/0.4 = 20.
Fan-out (high) = 0.4/(20 × 10⁻³) = 20.
Therefore, fan-out = 20   (*Ans.*)

Power Dissipation

Power is dissipated within a transistor as it switches from one state to another and also within all current-carrying resistors. The greater the power dissipation of a gate, the more heat must be removed from the circuit; also, particularly if many gates are used within an equipment, larger and hence more costly power supplies will be necessary.

The **dc power dissipation** of a gate is the product of the dc power supply voltage and the mean current taken from that supply.

Noise Immunity or Margin

Noise is the general term for any unwanted voltages that appear at the input to a gate. If the noise voltage has a sufficiently large amplitude, it may cause the gate to change its output state even though the input signal voltage has remained constant. Such false operation of a gate will lead to errors in the circuit performance. The **noise immunity** or **noise margin** of a gate is the maximum noise voltage that can appear at its input terminals without producing a change in the output state. Usually, manufacturers of integrated circuit gates quote d.c. values of noise margin, giving both typical and worst case values.

The **threshold value** of a gate is the input voltage at which a change of the output state of the circuit is just triggered. A reasonable approximation to this value is the voltage midway between the two logic levels. For the ttl logic family the threshold voltage is 1.4 V but the maximum input voltage that will definitely be read as logic 0 is 800 mV, whilst the minimum input voltage giving a definite logic 1 is 2.0 V.

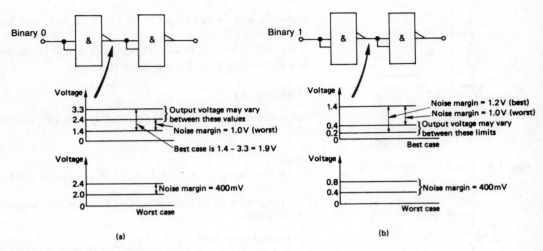

Fig. 4.5 Noise margin of TTL gates

The noise margin of a gate is equal to the difference between the logic level at the output of the gate and the threshold value of the gate(s) to which its output is connected. This is shown by Fig. 4.5 which refers to TTL NAND gates. In Fig. 4.5 it is supposed that binary 0 is applied to the inputs of the first NAND gate so that its output is at binary 1. This means that the output voltage lies within the limits of 2.4 V and 3.3 V. The threshold voltage is taken as 1.4 V and so the noise margin varies between 1.0 V at the worst and 1.9 V at best. The maximum value of the threshold voltage is 2.0 V, and should this exist the worst-case noise margin will be only 400 mV.

When the output of the first gate is at binary 0 its voltage will be within the range 0.2 V–0.4 V. The threshold voltage is 1.4 V and so the noise margin varies from 1.0 V at worst to 1.2 V at best. The minimum threshold voltage is only 0.8 V and hence the worst-case noise margin is 400 mV.

Gates in the CMOS family can be operated with a wide range of supply voltages (3–15 V or 2–6 V for hCMOS).

Transistor-Transistor Logic

The most popular and widely used logic family is known as transistor-transistor or TTL. The popularity of this logic family arises because it offers a good performance, it is readily available from several sources, and is easily interconnected or *interfaced* with other digital circuitry — all at a relatively low cost. The standard TTL logic, known as the 54/74 series, has a poor noise immunity and a rather high power consumption. The 74 series is designed for commercial applications and operates at ambient temperatures of up to 70 °C. The 54 series is primarily intended for military circuitry and has a maximum ambient temperature of 125 °C. Other versions of the TTL gates are also available.

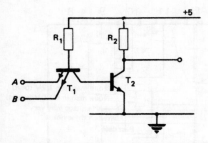

Fig. 4.6 Basic TTL NAND gate

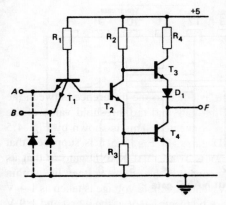

Fig. 4.7 Standard TTL NAND gate

NAND Gate

The basic circuit of a TTL NAND gate is given in Fig. 4.6. The input transistor has a number of emitters equal to the desired fan-in of the circuit; in the figure, a fan-in of 2 has been assumed. In the 54/74 series, fan-ins of 2, 3, 4 and 8 are available. When both input terminals are at +5 V the emitter/base junction of T_1 is reverse biased but its collector/base junction is forward biased. Current then flows from the collector power supply, through R_1, into the base of T_2. Transistor T_2 turns full ON and the output voltage of the circuit falls to the saturation voltage of the transistor. The output of the circuit is then at logic 0. When either or both of the input terminals is at approximately zero volts, logic 0, the associated emitter/base junction will be forward biased (its base is more positive than its emitter). The value of resistor R_1 is selected to ensure that T_1 is then full ON and so the base voltage of T_1 is only V_{BE1} volts (approximately 0.7 V) above earth potential. This potential is insufficient to keep T_2 ON and so T_2 turns OFF. The output voltage of the circuit then rises to +5 V, i.e. becomes logic 1. Thus, transistor T_1 performs the AND function and T_2 acts as an inverter to give an overall circuit rendering of the NAND function.

The standard TTL gate adds an output stage to the basic circuit of Fig. 4.6 in order to increase both the operating speed and the fan-out, the complete circuit being given in Fig. 4.7. The output stage, consisting of transistors T_3 and T_4 and diode D_1, is often known as a *totem-pole* stage. When T_2 has turned ON the base/emitter potential of T_3 is approximately zero and so T_3 does not conduct. At the same time T_4 is turned ON by the voltage developed across resistor R_3. Thus, when T_2 is ON transistor T_3 is OFF and T_4 is ON; this means that the potential at the output terminal of the circuit is low and so the output state is logic 0. The fan-out can be up to about 10 without the saturation voltage of T_4 rising above the 0 level. Similarly, when T_2 is OFF its collector voltage is +5 V and its emitter voltage is 0 V. Now T_4 is turned OFF and T_3 conducts to an extent that is determined by the external load connected to the output terminals of the circuit. The output voltage is then equal to 5 V minus the voltage dropped across T_3 and D_1, i.e. logic 1. T_3 acts as an active pull-up resistor.

To protect the circuit from damage by any negative voltages arriving at the input terminals, and also to improve the noise immunity, a diode can be connected between each input and earth, shown dotted in Fig. 4.7.

Many IC packages contain more than one gate and some examples have their pin connections shown by Fig. 4.8.

The circuit diagram of a TTL NOR gate is given by Fig. 4.9. If either T_2 or T_3 is turned ON, the base potential of T_5 will fall to very nearly 0 V and T_5 will turn OFF. Since either T_2 or T_3 is conducting heavily, the positive voltage developed across R_3 will be large enough to turn T_6 ON; then the output of the circuit will be at logic

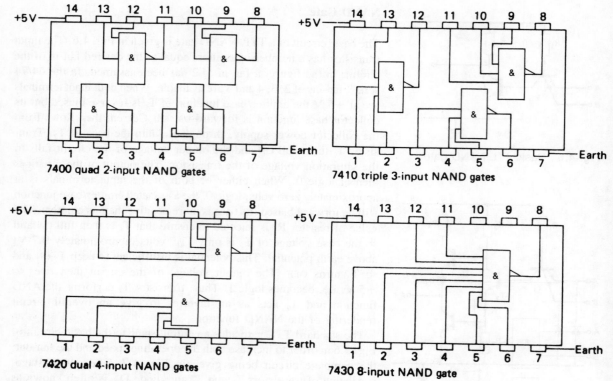

Fig. 4.8 Pin connections of four TTL IC gates

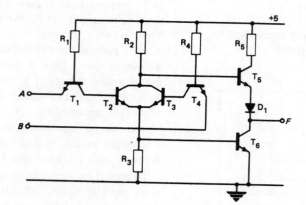

Fig. 4.9 TTL NOR gate

0. The output of the circuit will only be at logic 1 when both T_2 and T_3 are OFF; then the base potential of T_5 is +5 V and T_5 turns full ON, while T_6 is turned OFF because the voltage across R_3 is zero. Transistors T_2 and T_3 will be turned ON by a positive voltage at their base terminal and this will happen only if T_1 and/or T_4 is conducting, i.e. when input A and/or B is at +5 V or logic 1. The circuit therefore performs the NOR function since the output is at logic 1 only when both inputs A and B are at logic 0.

Open-collector Gates

Very often it is desirable to be able to connect together the outputs of several gates to increase the fan-out, or to perform a particular logical function, or perhaps to connect several gates to a common output line or *bus*.

If two gates with totem-pole output stages have their output terminals connected together, one of the gates is very likely to pass an excessive current which may well damage it. If, for example, the output of one gate is at logic 0, while the output of the other gate is at logic 1, the first gate would have a low resistance to earth and a current of high enough magnitude to cause damage could flow.

An **open-collector gate** is one which has been designed to permit it to be directly connected to another gate in the manner shown by Fig. 4.10. Two open-collector NAND gates have their output terminals paralleled and then connected to an external *pull-up resistor* R_1 to produce what is generally called the **wired-OR gate**. The logical function performed by a wired-OR gate is

$$F = \overline{AB} + \overline{CD}$$

If the same function is produced using totem-pole output stages, an extra gate is necessary, thus increasing the propagation delay (also the power dissipation is larger). Disadvantages of open-collector gates are: external pull-up resistor needed, and poorer noise margin.

The connection is known as the wired-OR because, if the output of either gate goes to zero volts, the output of the paralleled gates must also become 0 V. Only if both outputs are at logic 1 can the combined output be 1. The method of connection can be extended to more than two open-collector gates.

The wired-OR principle can be applied to form an exclusive-OR gate (see Fig. 4.11). For this circuit,

$$F = \overline{AB} + \overline{\overline{A}\,\overline{B}}$$
$$= \overline{(AB)}(\overline{\overline{A}\,\overline{B}})$$
$$= (\overline{A} + \overline{B})(A + B)$$
$$= \overline{A}A + \overline{A}B + A\overline{B} + B\overline{B}$$
$$= \overline{A}B + A\overline{B} \quad \text{the exclusive-OR function}$$

An open-collector gate differs from the totem-pole output equivalent in that the components R_4, T_3, D_1 in Fig. 4.7 are omitted. The pull-up resistor is necessary to ensure that the output terminal goes high when the output transistor T_4 (Fig. 4.7) turns OFF.

The value of the pull-up resistor R_1 depends upon the number N of open-collector gates that are connected together and the required fan-out n. The *minimum* value which R_1 can have is set by the wanted fan-out since the total current taken from a gate must not exceed 8 mA (LS TTL). Therefore,

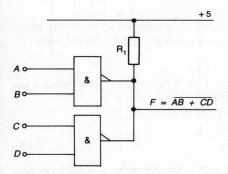

Fig. 4.10 Direct connection of open-collector gates

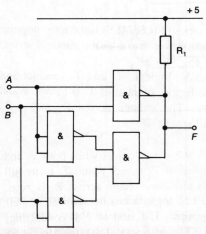

Fig. 4.11 Exclusive-OR gate using open-collector gates

$$R_{1(min)} = \frac{V_{CC} - \text{maximum 0 state output voltage}}{8 \text{ mA} - n \times \text{input current for the 0 state}}$$

$$= \frac{5 - 0.4}{8 - 1.6n} \text{ k}\Omega \tag{4.1}$$

The maximum value for the pull-up resistor is found by considering the output of a gate when at the logic 1 level. The current through R_1 will then be the sum of the currents supplied to the OFF outputs (a maximum of 250 μA in LS TTL) and the input current of the next stage (a maximum of 40 μA per gate for LS TTL). Therefore

$$R_{1(max)} = \frac{V_{CC} - \text{minimum 1 state output voltage}}{N \times 250 \ \mu\text{A} + n \times 40 \ \mu\text{A}}$$

$$= \frac{5 - 2.4}{0.25N + 0.04n} \text{ k}\Omega \tag{4.2}$$

EXAMPLE 4.2

Calculate the maximum and minimum values for the pull-up resistor in a wired-OR circuit if three NAND gates are connected and the fan-out is one.

Solution

$$R_{1(min)} = \frac{5 - 0.4}{8 - 1.6} = 719 \ \Omega$$

$$R_{1(max)} = \frac{5 - 2.4}{0.75 + 0.04} = 3291 \ \Omega$$

In most cases a 1000 Ω resistor is deemed to be a suitable value.

Low-Power Schottky TTL

The low-power Schottky TTL series (54LS/74LS) is the most popular TTL family since it dissipates less power than does the standard series. The NAND gate is shown in Fig. 4.12.

When both inputs are at +5 V, logic 1, T_1 and T_2 conduct and cause T_3/T_4 to conduct. The collector potential of T_3 is then low and this causes T_5/T_6 to turn OFF. The voltage across R_4 makes T_7 conduct to take the output to logic 0.

Advanced Schottky TTL

The latest developments in the TTL logic family have led to the introduction of two newer sub-groups. The first of these, known as advanced low-power Schottky TTL (ALS series), has been developed from the LS series. Compared with low-power Schottky it gives a two-fold reduction in both propagation delay and power dissipation.

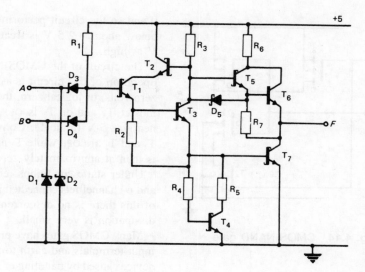

Fig. 4.12 Low-power Schottky TTL NAND gate

Also available is the advanced Schottky TTL family. This has evolved from Schottky TTL (S series) to give the family a higher operating speed than other forms of TTL. However, the penalty paid is a relatively high power dissipation. One form of the AS family is called FAST by its manufacturer (Fairchild). Both versions of advanced TTL provide a greatly increased *speed−power product*; this is the speed in nanoseconds multiplied by the power dissipation in milliwatts.

The number of devices presently manufactured in the advanced series is already quite large and is continually being increased. Generally, the AS and/or the ALS family can replace standard, S or LS devices in circuit designs except for the higher frequency applications.

CMOS Logic

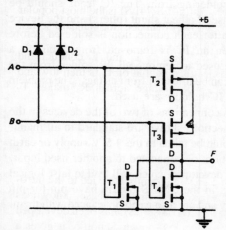

Fig. 4.13 CMOS NOR gate

The complementary metal-oxide semiconductor, or CMOS, logic family (4000 series) offers the desirable features of very low power dissipation and good noise immunity. The family finds particular application when low-power consumption is of prime importance. The main disadvantage associated with this type of gate has been its limited switching speed arising from the very high input impedance of a mosfet device. The 74C series of CMOS devices is both pin and number campatible with the 74 TTL family.

Figure 4.13 shows the circuit diagram of a CMOS NOR gate. If either input terminal A or input terminal B or both is at $+5$ V (logic 1) the associated p-channel mosfet (T_2 and/or T_3) is turned OFF, and the associated n-channel mosfet is turned ON. The drain/source voltages of T_1 and T_4 are then approximately zero and so the output state of the circuit is logical zero. If both input terminals A and B are at logic 0, mosfets T_1 and T_4 turn OFF. The output terminal of the circuit is now at very nearly $+5$ V and so the output state is logic 1. The output of the gate is logic 1 only when both inputs are at logic

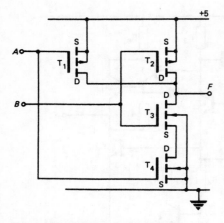

Fig. 4.14 CMOS NAND gate

0 and so the circuit performs the NOR function. Any input signal below about +2.5 V is treated as low and any signal above +2.5 V as high.

The circuit of the CMOS NAND gate is given in Fig. 4.14. The operation of this circuit is as follows. If either A or B or both is at zero volts, or logical zero, then mosfet T_1 and/or T_2 is turned ON but mosfet T_3 and/or T_4 is OFF. The output terminal is then at very nearly +5 V (logic 1). Conversely, if both A and B are at +5 V, T_1 and T_2 are OFF while T_3 and T_4 are ON. The output of the circuit is then at approximately zero volts or logic 0.

Under static conditions, either one or the other of the n-channel and p-channel fets connected across the power supply is OFF. Because of this there is no dc current through the circuit and so the power dissipation is very small.

Many CMOS gates have protective diodes connected between their input terminals and earth to reduce the possibility of damage to the device caused by handling or soldering. The gate terminal of a mosfet is insulated from the channel by a very thin layer of insulation which effectively forms the dielectric of a capacitance. Any electric charge which accumulates on the gate terminal may easily produce a voltage that is large enough to cause the dielectric to break down. Once this happens the device has been destroyed. The charge necessary to damage a mosfet need not be very large since the capacitance between the gate and the channel is very small and $V = Q/C$. This means that a dangerously high voltage can easily be produced by merely touching the gate lead with a finger or a tool. Great care must therefore be taken when a CMOS circuit is fitted into, or is removed from, a circuit. The leads of a CMOS device in store are usually short-circuited together by springy-wire clips or by conductive jelly or grease, and the short circuit should be maintained while the device is being fitted into circuit, particularly during the soldering process. The solderer should stand on a non-conducting surface such as a rubber mat and should use a non-earthed soldering iron. The IC leads should be protected from heat by the use of a heat shunt (pliers) and the device should be allowed to cool after each connection is soldered before tackling another one. When an IC is removed from a circuit a de-soldering tool should be used to remove all the solder from the connections and then the IC can be lifted off from its tags. The problem is, of course, simplified if IC holders are used.

Figure 4.15 shows the pin connections of two of the devices in the CMOS family; the pin connections shown are standard to all manufacturers. Unused inputs should be taken to the +5 V supply or earth depending on the logic function, or connected to another used input. Otherwise potentials may be developed which will lead to false logical operation of the gate. Gates in the CMOS family have pin-for-pin equivalents in the TTL family and are also easily interfaced with them.

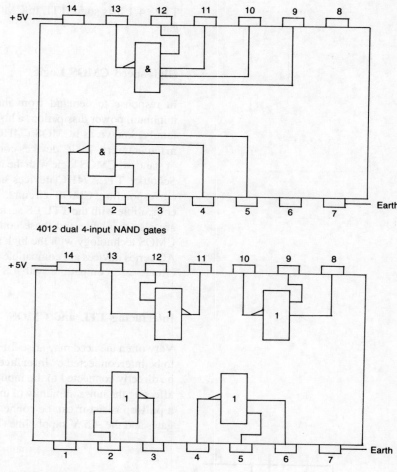

4012 dual 4-input NAND gates

4001 quad 2-input NOR gates

Fig. 4.15 Pin connections of two CMOS packages

Table 4.1 Functionally equivalent TTL/CMOS gates

Function	TTL	CMOS	Function	TTL	CMOS
Quad 2-input NAND	7400	4011	Quad 2-input NOR	7402	4001
Quad 2-input AND	7408	4081	Triple 3-input NAND	7410	4023
Triple 3-input NOR	7411	4073	Double 4-input NAND	7420	4012

Table 4.1 lists some TTL to CMOS functionally equivalent types of gate.

High-speed CMOS Logic

In response to demand from industry for fast logic devices with minimum power dissipation, a high-speed version of the CMOS logic family, known as hCMOS (74HC series) is now offered by several manufacturers. 74HC devices combine the low-power characteristics of standard CMOS logic with the high speed of operation of low-power Schottky TTL. 74HC devices are pin-for-pin compatible with the corresponding CMOS circuits. The 74HCT series is pin-for-pin compatible with the TTL LS series. Advanced hCMOS logic circuits are also available and these combine the low-power dissipation of CMOS technology with the high speed of advanced TTL technology. AC series devices are compatible with CMOS devices and ACT series circuits are compatible with LS TTL devices.

Interfacing TTL and CMOS

Very often the need may arise for gates in the TTL and CMOS families to be interconnected or **interfaced**. The output of a TTL gate cannot be directly connected to the input of a CMOS gate without adversely affecting the noise immunity of the circuit. To overcome this problem, a **pull-up resistor** can be connected between the junction of the two gates and the +5 V supply line (Fig. 4.16a). It is possible to directly

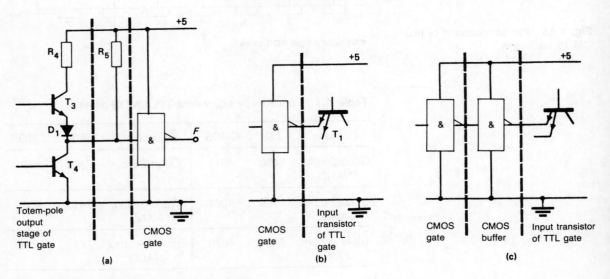

Fig. 4.16 Interfacing TTL and CMOS gates

connect the output of a CMOS gate to the input of a TTL gate as shown by Fig. 4.16*b*, but generally a CMOS buffer stage, such as the 4010, is used (Fig. 4.16*c*).

Emitter-coupled Logic

The main feature of emitter-coupled logic, or ECL, is the very fast speed of operation that is provided. This logic family is used when the maximum possible speed is the prime consideration. Very fast operation is obtained by designing the circuitry to ensure that the transistors do not drive into saturation when conducting. The basic ECL gate in the 10*K* series is a combined OR/NOR circuit and this, in common with the rest of the family, is operated from a −5.2 V supply. This means that logic 1 is represented by −0.9 V and logic 0 by −1.75 V.

The circuit diagram of an OR/NOR ECL gate is given by Fig. 4.17. A reference voltage of −1.29 V is developed by the R_7, D_1, D_2, R_8 circuit; and applied to the base terminal of transistor T_3. If both inputs A and B are at logical zero (−1.75 V) then the base potential of T_3 is more positive (less negative) than the base potentials of either T_1 or T_2, and so T_3 conducts whilst T_1 and T_2 do not. The collector current of T_3 develops a voltage of about −1.0 V across R_5 and this causes T_5 to conduct. T_5 is connected as an emitter follower and so its output voltage is $-1.0 \text{ V} - V_{BE5} \simeq -1.7 \text{ V}$ which represents logic 0. The collector potentials of T_1 and T_2 are approximately zero and hence the output voltage of T_6 is $0 \text{ V} - V_{BE6} \simeq -0.7 \text{ V}$ which represents logic 1.

If either input A or B is at logic 1, i.e. −0.9 V, the associated transistor is turned ON while T_3 is turned OFF. Now the collector potentials of T_1/T_2 and T_3 are reversed compared to the previous case and so now, T_5 output is at logic 1 and T_6 output is at logic 0.

Since each input is terminated by a resistor, an unused input need not be connected to a fixed voltage level.

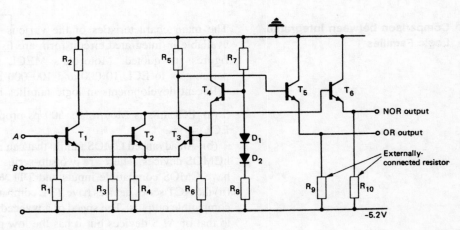

Fig. 4.17 ECL 10 K OR/NOR gate

Table 4.2   Integrated circuit logic families

Logic family	Propagation delay (ns)	Power dissipation (mW)	Noise margin (mV) 1	Noise margin (mV) 0	Fan-out	Supply voltage (V)	Maximum frequency (MHz)	Logic levels (V) V_{IH} (min)	V_{IL} (max)	V_{OH} (min)	V_{OL} (max)
Standard TTL	10	10	400	400	10	5	35	2	0.8	2.4	0.4
Low-power Schottky TTL	10	2	700	400	20	5	40	2	0.8	2.7	0.4
Advanced Schottky TTL	1.7	8	400	300	40	5	200	2	0.8	2.4	0.5
Advanced low-power Schottky TTL	4	1	700	400	40	5	70	2	0.8	2.7	0.4
CMOS 4000	50	1×10^{-3}	29% V_{DD}	29% V_{DD}	10	3–15	12	depends on V_{DD}			
hCMOS	10	2.5×10^{-6}	28% V_{DD}	18% V_{DD}	10	2–6	40	depends on V_{DD}			
ECL 10 000	2	25	400	400	50	−5.2		−1.1	−2.5	−2.2	−1.0
ECL 100 000	0.75	40	400	400	50	−4.5		as 10 000			

The ECL 10 000 series uses a −5.2 V supply; the even faster 100 000 series uses a −4.5 V supply and a different circuit for the OR/NOR gate.

When an ECL circuit is to interface with CMOS or TTL circuitry, the connection must be made via a *level shifting circuit* because of the −5.2 V supply voltage of ECL. Level shifter circuits are available in the CMOS family, e.g. 4049/50.

Comparison between Integrated Logic Families

The main characteristics of the various logic families which are available in integrated circuit form are listed in Table 4.2. Typical figures are quoted. Motorola's MECL II/III family has similar parameters to ECL 10 000 and 100 000 respectively.

Recent developments in logic families include:

(a) ECLinPs is Motorola's 500 ps propagation delay, 800 MHz ECL series.

(b) An advanced CMOS family that can replace LS, ALS, AS, and hCMOS devices. There are two sub-series: (i) the AC series devices have CMOS compatible inputs and TTL/MOS compatible outputs; (ii) the ACT series devices have TTL compatible inputs and TTL/MOS compatible outputs. The speed of advanced CMOS circuits is similar to that of ALS devices but it has the low power dissipation and the high noise immunity of CMOS.

(c) Bus structures employ bus interface devices, such as latches, drivers and transceivers, and these can, with advantage, use the new BiCMOS logic. BiCMOS offers a combination of the best features of both the TTL and the CMOS technologies giving high speed, high current output, high-impedance outputs when the device is disabled, and low power dissipation.

Systems such as mainframe computers where the highest possible speed of operation is of the utmost importance use ECL but most other systems use one form or other of TTL or CMOS.

5 MSI Combinational Logic Circuits

A combinational logic circuit is one whose output, or outputs, are determined by the logic states of its existing input, or inputs. This is to be contrasted with *sequential logic* circuits whose output is set by *both* the present input state *and* the previous output state of the circuit.

Many different combinational logic circuits are possible and they find a wide variety of applications, some of which have been discussed in the previous chapters. In many cases it is not necessary to design and construct the required circuit using gates of one kind or another. Instead, a medium-scale integrated circuit (MSI) can be employed. The MSI combinational logic circuits to be considered in this chapter are multiplexers, demultiplexers, code converters and binary adders, since they are probably the most commonly employed.

Multiplexers

A *multiplexer*, or *data selector*, is a circuit whose basic function is to select any one out of *n* input lines and to transmit the data present on that line to a single output line. The basic concept is illustrated by Fig. 5.1. At any instant in time only one of the switches is closed connecting the associated data input to the output.

The digital equivalent to Fig. 5.1 can be built using a number of gates but, in practice, an MSI device would be chosen. Several different multiplexers are listed in the TTL, CMOS and the ECL logic families; some examples are:

TTL   74151 8-to-1 multiplexer, 74153 dual 4-to-1 multiplexer

CMOS   4512 8-to-1 multiplexer, 4539   dual 4-to-1 multiplexer

hCMOS 74151 8-to-1 multiplexer, 74153 dual 4-to-1 multiplexer

ECL   10164 8-to-1 multiplexer, 10174 dual 4-to-1 multiplexer

The pin connections and the logic symbol of the 74153 circuit are given in Fig. 5.2, and the truth table for each multiplexer is listed by Table 5.1.

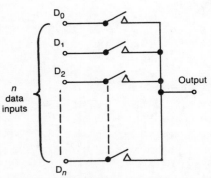

Fig. 5.1 Multiplexer principle

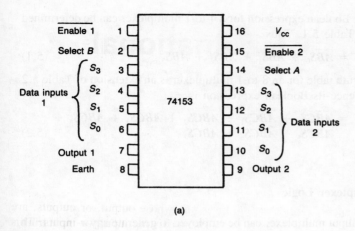

Fig. 5.2 (a) Pin connections and (b) logic symbol of the 74153 dual 4-to-1 multiplexer

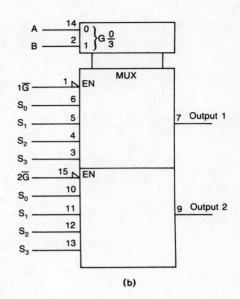

Table 5.1

Inputs							Output
Select		Data				Enable	
B	A	S_3	S_2	S_1	S_0		
X	X	X	X	X	X	1	0
0	0	X	X	X	0	0	0
0	0	X	X	X	1	0	1
0	1	X	X	0	X	0	0
0	1	X	X	1	X	0	1
1	0	X	0	X	X	0	0
1	0	X	1	X	X	0	1
1	1	0	X	X	X	0	0
1	1	1	X	X	X	0	1

As before, X indicates don't care.

When the enable input is high the output will be low whatever the state of the other inputs. When the enable input is low the control of the circuit operation is passed to the other inputs. The select inputs A and B control *both* circuits and are employed to select one of the data inputs S_0, S_1, S_2 and S_3 and cause its logical state to become the output state of the multiplexer. Consider, for example, row 5 of the truth table: in this $A = 1$, $B = 0$ so that input S_1 is selected; the logical state of S_1 is 1 so that the output state becomes 1 also.

The Boolean expression for a 4-to-1 multiplexer can be determined from Table 5.1. Thus

$$F = \bar{A}\bar{B}S_0 + A\bar{B}S_1 + \bar{A}BS_2 + ABS_3 \qquad (5.1)$$

The truth table for an 8-to-1 multiplexer is an extension of Table 5.2 and hence its Boolean expression is

$$F = \bar{A}\bar{B}\bar{C}S_0 + A\bar{B}\bar{C}S_1 + \bar{A}B\bar{C}S_2 + AB\bar{C}S_3 + \bar{A}\bar{B}CS_4 + A\bar{B}CS_5 + \bar{A}BCS_6 + ABCS_7 \qquad (5.2)$$

Multiplexer Logic

An n-input multiplexer can be employed to generate any n-input truth table and therefore to implement a Boolean equation. The number of select inputs must be one less than the number of input variables or literals. The least significant bit of the function to be implemented determines the signal to be applied to each data input while the more significant bits are applied to the select inputs.

EXAMPLE 5.1

Use a multiplexer to implement the logical function

$$F = \bar{A}\bar{B}C + \bar{A}\bar{B}\bar{C} + A\bar{B}C + AB\bar{C}$$

Solution
Comparing the function to be implemented with equation (5.1),

$$\bar{A}\bar{B}: S_0 = C + \bar{C} = 1$$
$$A\bar{B}: S_1 = C$$
$$\bar{A}B: S_2 = 0 \quad \text{(no } \bar{A}B \text{ term)}$$
$$\bar{A}B: S_3 = \bar{C}$$

Figure 5.3 shows the required implementation.

EXAMPLE 5.2

Use a multiplexer to implement the logical function

$$F = \bar{A}\bar{B}\bar{C}\bar{D} + A\bar{B}\bar{C}D + \bar{A}\bar{B}CD + \bar{A}B\bar{C}D + ABCD + A\bar{B}C\bar{D}$$

Solution
There are 4 input variables or literals so a multiplexer with 3 select terminals is necessary, i.e. an 8-to-1 multiplexer. Comparing the equation to be implemented with equation (5.2),

$$\bar{A}\bar{B}\bar{C}: S_0 = \bar{D}, \ A\bar{B}\bar{C}: S_1 = D, \ \bar{A}B\bar{C}: S_2 = 0$$
$$AB\bar{C}: S_3 = 0, \ \bar{A}\bar{B}C: S_4 = \bar{D}, \ A\bar{B}C: S_5 = \bar{D}$$
$$\bar{A}BC: S_6 = D, \ ABC: S_7 = D$$

The multiplexer implementation of the function is shown by Fig. 5.4.

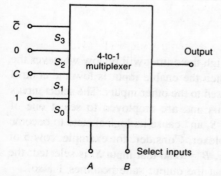

Fig. 5.3

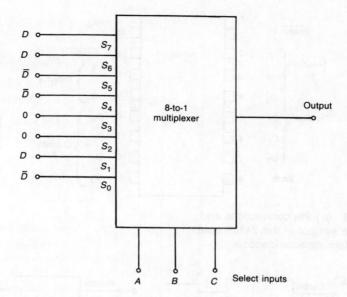

Fig. 5.4

Demultiplexers and Decoders

A demultiplexer performs the inverse function to a multiplexer in that it has a single input terminal and effectively switches it to any one of a number of possible outputs. The required output is selected by an input address. Non-selected outputs are either non-active or are open-circuit.

A decoder performs a similar function but the *only* input is the address of the output to be selected.

The basic idea of a demultiplexer can best be understood by reference to Fig. 5.5. Clearly, any one of the four outputs can be connected to the input.

Examples of demultiplexers in the logic families are:

TTL	74138	1-of-8 demultiplexer/decoder
	74139	dual 1-of-4 demultiplexer/decoder
CMOS	4514	1-of-16 demultiplexer with input latches
	45555	dual 1-of-4 demultiplexer/decoder
hCMOS	138	1-of-8 demultiplexer/decoder
	139	dual 1-of-4 demultiplexer/decoder
ECL	10161	1-of-8 decoder
	10171	dual 1-of-4 decoder.

Consider, as one of the simpler examples, the TTL 74139 1-of-4 demultiplexer/decoder. Figure 5.6 shows the pin connections and the logic symbol, and Table 5.2 the truth table, of the device.

Each of the two circuits in the IC package has one enable, and two select input pins and four output pins. When the enable pin is high all four outputs are also high, regardless of the logical state of the select inputs. When the enable pin is low *only* the output selected by the input address pins A and B will be low.

When the circuit is employed as a demultiplexer the enable pin is used as the data input terminal. The output that is selected by the input

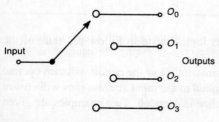

Fig. 5.5 Demultiplexer principle

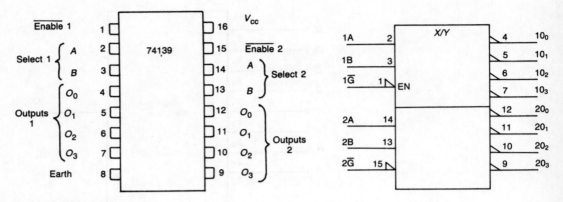

Fig. 5.6 (a) Pin connections and (b) logic symbol of the 74139 dual 1-of-4 demultiplexer/decoder

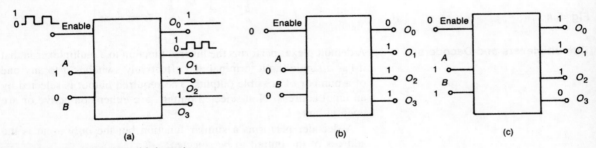

Fig. 5.7 Use of a demultiplexer/decoder as (a) a demultiplexer, (b) and (c) as a decoder

Table 5.2 (for each decoder)

Inputs			Outputs			
Enable	Select		O_3	O_2	O_1	O_0
	B	A				
1	X	X	1	1	1	1
0	0	0	1	1	1	0
0	0	1	1	1	0	1
0	1	0	1	0	1	1
0	1	1	0	1	1	1

address (AB) will change its logical state to follow the state of the input data, Fig. 5.7a.

If the enable pin is held permanently low the circuit will then operate as a decoder. The signals applied to the input address pins will ensure that only the required output line is decoded. Two examples are given in Figs 5.7b and c.

Code Converters

A code converter is a circuit that takes an input in one code and produces an output in some other code. It is usual to refer to code converters as decoders and some examples follow.

TTL	7442	BCD-to-decimal decoder,	7443 Excess 3-to-decimal decoder
	7447	BCD-to-7 segment decoder	
CMOS	4028	BCD-to-decimal decoder,	4511 BCD-to-7 segment decoder
hCMOS	HCT42	BCD-to-decimal decoder	

The operation of each of these devices is fully explained by its truth table and, as an example, Table 5.3 gives the truth table for the 7442. Figure 5.8 gives the pin connections of the IC.

The circuit has four input lines and 10 output lines. When a BCD number (between 0 and 9) is applied to the input pins the appropriate decimal output pin goes low.

Table 5.3

Decimal	BCD input				Decimal output									
	D	C	B	A	9	8	7	6	5	4	3	2	1	0
0	0	0	0	0	1	1	1	1	1	1	1	1	1	0
1	0	0	0	1	1	1	1	1	1	1	1	1	0	1
2	0	0	1	0	1	1	1	1	1	1	1	0	1	1
3	0	0	1	1	1	1	1	1	1	1	0	1	1	1
9	1	0	0	1	0	1	1	1	1	1	1	1	1	1

10–15 are don't cares

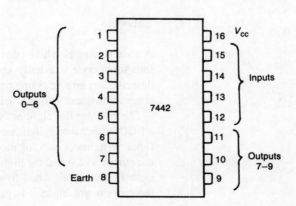

Fig. 5.8 Pin connections of the 7442 BCD-to-decimal decoder

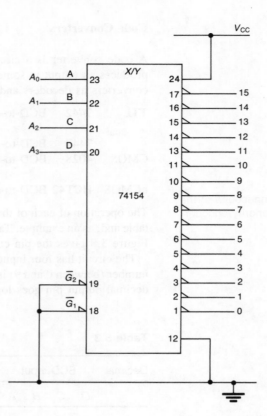

Fig. 5.9 The LS74154 4-to-16 line decoder used as a binary-to-hex converter

A 4-to-16 line decoder can be used as a binary-to-hexadecimal converter. Figure 5.9 shows how the LS74154 is connected for this purpose. Each output, 0 through to 15, is normally high but goes low when it is selected by the digital word applied to the inputs A_0, A_1, A_2 and A_3. The two enable pins $\bar{G}_1$ and $\bar{G}_2$ can be connected to earth as shown, or they may have the clock connected to them to prevent glitches occurring.

Encoders

A code converter which converts from either decimal or hexadecimal into some code is usually known as an *encoder*. The TTL 74148 is described as an 8-to-3 line priority encoder. Figure 5.10 gives its pin connections and Table 5.4 its truth table.

The encoder has eight active low inputs and its action is to provide a BCD output which indicates the position of the highest order active input. Whenever two, or more, inputs are at logic 0 simultaneously the output will signal the highest priority input. The enable in terminal enables the circuit when low and the enable out goes low when all the outputs are high; it is used for cascading two ICs. The GS pin

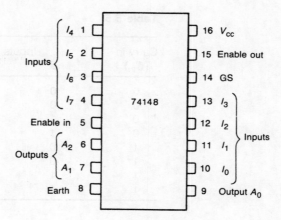

Fig. 5.10 Pin connections of the 74148 8-to-3 line priority encoder

Table 5.4

Enable in	Inputs								Outputs				Enable out
	I_7	I_6	I_5	I_4	I_3	I_2	I_1	I_0	GS	A_2	A_1	A_0	
1	X	X	X	X	X	X	X	X	1	1	1	1	1
0	1	1	1	1	1	1	1	1	1	1	1	1	0
0	X	X	X	X	X	X	X	0	0	0	0	0	1
0	X	X	X	X	X	X	0	1	0	1	0	0	1
0	X	X	X	X	X	0	1	1	0	0	1	0	1
0	X	X	X	X	0	1	1	1	0	1	1	0	1
0	X	X	X	0	1	1	1	1	0	0	0	1	1
0	X	X	0	1	1	1	1	1	0	1	0	1	1
0	X	0	1	1	1	1	1	1	0	0	1	1	1
0	0	1	1	1	1	1	1	1	0	1	1	1	1

goes low when any input is active and it thus indicates the presence of an active input. The 74147 is a 10-to-4 line priority encoder.

Binary Adders

A binary adder is a circuit which is able to add together two binary numbers. The *half-adder* adds two inputs A and B to produce a *sum* and a *carry* but it is unable to take into account any carry from a previous stage. The half-adder was considered in Chapter 3. The full-adder also adds together two binary numbers but it can take account of any input carry as well. The truth table of a full-adder is given by Table 5.5.

The Boolean equation describing the logical operation of the full adder can be derived from the truth table. It is

$$S = \overline{A}\overline{B}\overline{C}_{IN} + \overline{A}B\overline{C}_{IN} + A\overline{B}C_{IN} + ABC_{IN}$$
$$= (A\overline{B} + \overline{A}B)\overline{C}_{IN} + (AB + \overline{A}\overline{B})C_{IN}$$
$$= (A \oplus B)\overline{C}_{IN} + (\overline{A \oplus B})C_{IN} \qquad (5.3)$$

Table 5.5

Carry in (C_{IN})	Inputs		Sum	Carry out (C_{OUT})
	B	A		
0	0	0	0	0
0	0	1	1	0
0	1	0	1	0
0	1	1	0	1
1	0	0	1	0
1	0	1	0	1
1	1	0	0	1
1	1	1	1	1

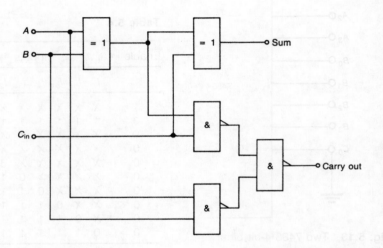

Fig. 5.11 Full adder

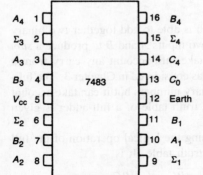

Fig. 5.12 Pin connections of the 7483 4-bit binary adder

$$C_{OUT} = AB\bar{C}_{IN} + A\bar{B}C_{IN} + \bar{A}BC_{IN} + ABC_{IN}$$
$$= AB + (A \oplus B)C_{IN} \tag{5.4}$$

The implementation of eqns (5.3) and (5.4) can be achieved using gates, see Fig. 5.11. Usually, however, two 4-bit numbers, or bigger, are to be added and then an MSI circuit is employed. Examples of MSI binary adders include:

TTL   7483   4-bit adder
CMOS   4004   4-bit adder
ECL   100180   6-bit adder.

The pin connections of the TTL 7483 are shown by Fig. 5.12. The 7483 is able to accept two 4-bit numbers A and B *and* a carry C_0 from a previous stage. The sum of the two numbers appears at the terminals labelled as Σ_1, Σ_2, Σ_3 and Σ_4 with any carry out appearing at terminal C_4. If (*a*) the sum of A and B and C_0 is anywhere between 0 and 15 the output carry C_4 will be 0; and if (*b*) the sum

Table 5.6

Input								C_0	Σ_4	Σ_3	Σ_2	Σ_1	C_4
A				B									
1	0	0	1	0	0	1	1	0	1	1	0	0	0
1	0	1	0	0	1	1	1	0	0	0	0	1	1
1	0	1	0	0	1	1	1	1	0	0	1	0	1

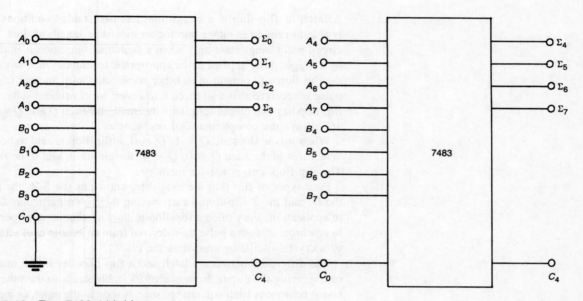

Fig. 5.13 Two 7483 4-bit binary adders connected to give 8-bit addition

of A and B and C_0 is anywhere between 16 and 31 the output carry is 1 and the Σ outputs indicate a number equal to the sum of A and B minus 16. Table 5.6 gives some examples.

Should the two numbers to be added have more than 4 bits two 7483s can be cascaded in the manner shown by Fig. 5.13 for 8-bit arithmetic. The carry-out C_4 of the least significant stage is connected to the carry-in C_0 of the next most significant stage.

6 Flip-flops

A **latch** or **flip-flop** is a circuit that has two stable conditions and is able to remain in either one for an indefinite length of time. The circuit will change state only when a switching operation is initiated by a trigger pulse applied to the appropriate terminal. Once switched the flip-flop will remain in its other stable state until another trigger pulse is received that will force it to revert to its original state. The flip-flop has two output terminals, normally labelled Q and $\bar{Q}$ which are always the complements of one another.

When it is in the state $Q = 1$, $\bar{Q} = 0$, a flip-flop is said to be *set*. When it is in the state $Q = 0$, $\bar{Q} = 1$, the circuit is said to be *reset*. The flip-flop acts as a 1-bit memory.

Four types of flip-flop are available, known as the S-R, the J-K, the D, and the T flip-flops, each having their own particular fields of application. Very often a flip-flop is *clocked*, that is, it is operated in synchronism with a pulse train derived from an astable multivibrator or a crystal oscillator known as the *clock*.

The difference between a latch and a flip-flop lies in the method of triggering the circuit from one of its stable states to the other. A non-synchronous latch will change state as soon as the input, or inputs, reach a valid voltage level. A clocked, or synchronous, latch will not change state until the circuit is *enabled* by the clock waveform being at the logic 1 voltage level. The output of the latch will follow the input(s) as long as the latch remains enabled. A latch is said to be level triggered.

A flip-flop is either a *master-slave* device (also known as pulse-triggered) or it is *edge-triggered*. Some edge-triggered circuits change state only when the clock waveform changes from 0 to 1 — known as leading edge-triggered — or as the clock waveform changes from 1 to 0 — known as trailing edge-triggered.

The S-R Flip-Flop

NON - SYNCHRONOUS

Set

Reset

Fig. 6.1 Symbol for an S-R flip-flop

The symbol for a non-synchronous S-R flip-flop is given in Fig. 6.1. The device has two input terminals labelled S and R and two output terminals labelled Q and $\bar{Q}$. Always the logical state of the $\bar{Q}$ output is the complement of the state of the Q terminal. The logical operation of an S-R flip-flop is summarized by its truth table, Table 6.1.

The symbol Q^+ represents the logical state of the Q output *after* a set (S) or a reset (R) pulse has been applied to the appropriate input

Table 6.1   S-R flip-flop

S	R	Q	Q^+
0	0	0	0
0	0	1	1
1	0	0	1
1	0	1	1
0	1	0	0
0	1	1	0
1	1	0	X
1	1	1	X

terminal. When $S = R = 0$ the state of the output will remain unchanged at whatever logical state it should already have. To *set* the circuit, that is to make $Q = 1$ and $\overline{Q} = 0$, requires $S = 1$, $R = 0$. If the circuit was already set before the S pulse is applied, the flip-flop will not switch. Similarly, to reset the circuit, $Q = 0$, $\overline{Q} = 1$, requires $S = 0$, $R = 1$. If pulses are simultaneously applied to both the set and the reset terminals, so that $S = R = 1$, the effect upon the circuit cannot be predicted; the flip-flop may switch to reverse the states of its two outputs or it may remain in its existing condition. The $S = R = 1$ condition is said to be *indeterminate*.

1   Figure 6.2*a* shows how an S-R flip-flop can be made by connecting together two NOR gates. The output of a 2-input NOR gate is 1 only when both of its inputs are at 0; if either or both of its inputs is at logic 1, the output state will be 0.

Suppose the circuit is initially set, i.e. $Q = 1$, $\overline{Q} = 0$. If $S = R = 0$ the upper gate will then have both of its inputs at 0 and so Q remains at 1. The lower gate has one input at 0 and the other at 1, hence its output $\overline{Q} = 0$. If now a pulse is applied to the input (reset) terminal only, giving $S = 0$, $R = 1$, the upper gate will have one input (R) at 1 and the other ($\overline{Q}$) at 0; the output (Q) of this gate will then become equal to logic 0. Both inputs to the lower gate are now at 0 and so the output of this gate, the $\overline{Q}$ terminal, becomes logic 1. Thus the circuit has switched states from $Q = 1$, $\overline{Q} = 0$ to $Q = 0$, $\overline{Q} = 1$, i.e. the flip-flop has been *reset*.

With the flip-flop in the reset condition, suppose that the input conditions change to $S = 1$, $R = 0$. The lower gate will now have one input (S) at 1 and the other (Q) at 0 and so its output ($\overline{Q}$) will be 0. This means that the upper gate now has both of its inputs at 0 and so its output (Q) becomes 1. The timing diagram is shown in Fig. 6.2*b*.

Whether the flip-flop is set or reset the application of a pulse to both the S and R inputs simultaneously may or may not switch the circuit; in other words the circuit's operation is indeterminate.

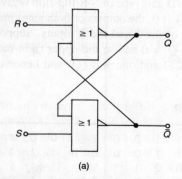

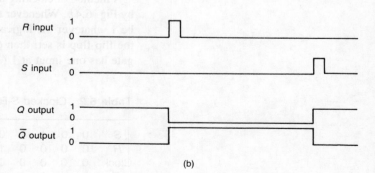

(a)   (b)

Fig. 6.2   (*a*) S-R flip-flop using two NOR gates, (*b*) timing diagram

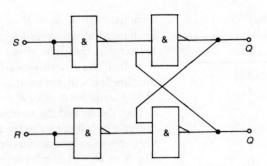

Fig. 6.3 S-R flip-flop using four NAND gates

2 The S-R flip-flop can also be constructed using four NAND gates interconnected in the manner shown in Fig. 6.3. The output of a NAND gate is 0 only if both of its input terminals are at 1; if either or both inputs is at 0, the output will be 1. Suppose that initially the flip-flop is set and $S = R = 0$. Both inputs to the lower gate are 1 and hence $\bar{Q}$ remains at 0. This means that the upper gate has one of its inputs $(\bar{S})$ at 1 and the $(\bar{Q})$ at 0 and so its output terminal remains at 1. Re-setting the circuit requires the input condition $S = 0$, $R = 1$. Then, the lower gate will have one input $(\bar{R})$ at 0 and its other input (Q) at 1 and so its output $(\bar{Q})$ will become 1. This results in the upper gate having both its inputs $(\bar{S}$ and $\bar{Q})$ at 1 and its output becomes $Q = 0$. To set the circuit $S = 1$, $R = 0$; then the upper gate has one input $(\bar{S})$ at 0 and the other $(\bar{Q})$ at 1 and hence its output is $Q = 1$. Finally, the lower gate has now both of its inputs at 1 and it switches to give $\bar{Q} = 0$. Once again the input state $S = R = 1$ is indeterminate and may result in the flip-flop either switching or its output state remaining unchanged.

3 Very often it is desirable for the set and reset operations to occur at particular instants in time determined by the *clock*. A *clocked* flip-flop will change state only when a clock pulse is received. The truth table of a clocked S-R flip-flop is given in Table 6.2 and its symbol in Fig. 6.4*a*.

A method of clocking the NAND gate type of S-R flip-flop is given by Fig. 6.4*b*. Whenever the clock is 0, the outputs of both gates must be 1 whatever the logical states of the S and the R inputs. Suppose the flip-flop is set; then $Q = 1$, $\bar{Q} = 0$ and so the upper right-hand gate has one input at 1 $(\bar{CS} + \bar{CS})$ and one at 0 $(\bar{Q})$ and hence the

Table 6.2 Clocked S-R flip-flop

S	0	0	1	1	0	0	1	1	0	0	1	1	0	0	1	1
R	0	0	0	0	1	1	1	1	0	0	0	0	1	1	1	1
Clock	0	0	0	0	0	0	0	0	1	1	1	1	1	1	1	1
Q	0	1	0	1	0	1	0	1	0	1	0	1	0	1	0	1
Q^+	0	1	0	1	0	1	0	1	0	1	1	1	0	0	X	X

SYMBOL

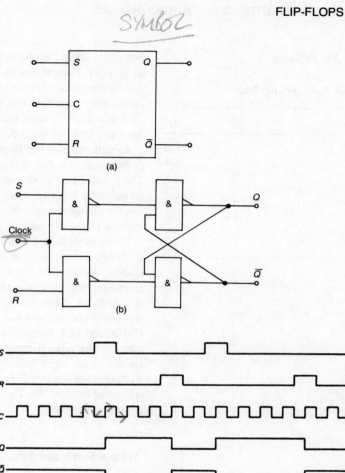

Fig. 6.4 Clocked S-R flip-flop, (a) symbol, (b) NAND version

Fig. 6.5 Waveforms in a clocked S-R flip-flop

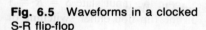

Q output remains at 1. The lower right-hand gate has both of its inputs at logic 1 and so the $\bar{Q}$ output remains unchanged at 0. Only when the clock input is 1 can the appropriate input gate (S or $R = 1$) have an output at 0 for a possible switching action to be initiated. In other words, when the clock input is at logic 1, the circuit follows the same sequence of operations as the basic NAND flip-flop of Fig. 6.3. The clock determines the times at which the S and R input signals should be effective and this is illustrated by the waveforms given in Fig. 6.5. It can be seen that the flip-flop does not set (or reset) immediately an S (or R) pulse is received but waits until the clock changes from 0 to 1.

Clocked operation of an S-R flip-flop, and of the other types of flip-flop discussed later in this chapter, ensures that all the flip-flops in a system operate in synchronism with one another. Synchronous operation of a digital system is generally advantageous since it

(*a*) leads to faster operation,
(*b*) avoids the transient problems which may arise in a non-synchronous system.

The J-K Flip-flop

Table 6.3 J-K flip-flop

J	K	Q	Q^+
0	0	0	0
0	0	1	1
1	0	0	1
1	0	1	1
0	1	0	0
0	1	1	0
1	1	0	1
1	1	1	0

changes state

X AVOID!

For many digital applications the indeterminate $S = R = 1$ state of an S-R flip-flop cannot be permitted and, when this is the case, an alternative circuit, known as the J-K flip-flop, can be used. The operational difference between the S-R and the J-K flip-flops lies in the final two rows of their truth tables. This can be seen by comparing the truth table of the J-K flip-flop (Table 6.3) with Table 6.1.

As with the S-R flip-flop the symbol Q^+ represents the state of the Q output after a J or K trigger pulse has been applied to the circuit. The J pulse acts as the set signal, and the K pulse acts as the reset signal. The last two rows of Table 6.3 show that the J-K flip-flop *always* changes state when *both* J and K pulses are simultaneously applied to the circuit.

The symbol for a J-K flip-flop is given in Fig. 6.6a. A clock input is shown since this type of flip-flop is normally operated synchronously. Very often, clear (or reset) terminals and perhaps preset terminals are also provided (Fig. 6.6b); these are always non-synchronous. The small triangles indicate that the clear and preset terminals are active low. J-K flip-flops are available in the TTL, CMOS and ECL families and are either *master-slave* or *edge-triggered* circuits. An edge-triggered flip-flop is indicated by a small wedge on the clock input (see Fig. 6.6c). No small triangle indicates a leading-edge-triggered, and a small triangle indicates a trailing-edge-triggered device, see Fig. 6.10. Most modern flip-flops are edge-triggered devices.

Master-Slave and Edge-triggered Flip-flops

When a flip-flop is synchronously operated, i.e. enabled by a clock pulse, the circuit must respond to any changes in the input signal that take place *during* the time that the clock is at 1. This means that the duration of a clock pulse must be less than the time it takes for the flip-flop to change state in response to an input trigger signal. This

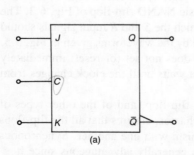

(a)

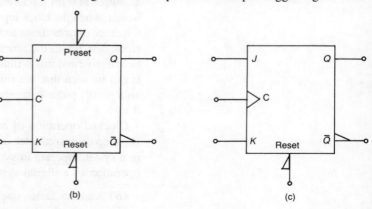

(b)   (c)

Fig. 6.6 Symbols for (a) a clocked J-K flip-flop, (b) a J-K flip-flop with clear and preset terminals, and (c) a leading-edge triggered J-K flip-flop

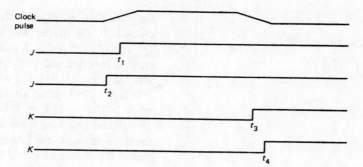

Fig. 6.7 Clock pulse rise-times and fall-times

often leads to practical difficulties, such as false switching, arising from the rise-times and fall-times of the clock pulses being insufficiently short. Thus, referring to Fig. 6.7, a J pulse occurring at time t_1 will probably set the flip-flop because at this instant in time the clock pulse has reached about 50% of its final voltage, but a J pulse arriving at time t_2 would not trigger the circuit because, although a clock pulse has arrived, its amplitude is still very small. Similarly, a K pulse initiated at time t_3 might well reset the circuit even though the clock pulse has ended because the fall-time of the clock pulse voltage is such that its value is still fairly large. A K pulse at time t_4, on the other hand, would not reset the circuit since the clock pulse voltage has by now decreased to very nearly zero.

The switching difficulties associated with clocked operation of a flip-flop can be overcome by either *master-slave* or *edge-triggered* circuitry.

Master-Slave J-K Flip-flop

The circuit of a master-slave J-K flip-flop is shown in Fig. 6.8. The left-hand flip-flop is the *master* and the right-hand flip-flop is the *slave*.

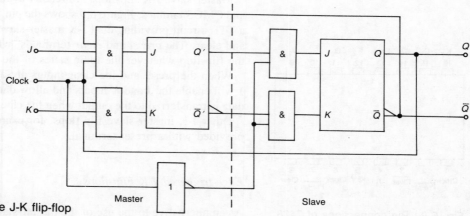

Fig. 6.8 Master-slave J-K flip-flop

Suppose that initially the flip-flop is set so that $Q = 1$. When the clock is 0, the master will have $J = K = 0$ and hence its outputs Q' and $\bar{Q}'$ remain at 1 and 0 respectively. The clock input to the slave is inverted and so the slave has $J = 1$, $K = 0$. This condition sets the slave to retain Q and $\bar{Q}$ at 1 and 0 respectively.

When a clock pulse arrives, $C = 1$, either J or K or both could be at 1. If $J = 1$, $K = 0$ both inputs to the master are at 0 (since $\bar{Q} = 0$) and switching is not initiated. Suppose that now $J = 0$, $K = 1$; the three inputs to the lower input AND gate are all at 1 and so the master flip-flop has inputs $J = 0$, $K = 1$ applied. The master therefore changes state to have $Q' = 0$, $\bar{Q}' = 1$. However, since the clock is inverted, this change of state cannot be passed on to the slave, both of whose inputs remain at 0, so that at the output the condition $Q = 1$, $\bar{Q} = 0$ is retained. At the end of the clock pulse $C = 0$ and now the lower slave input AND gate has both its inputs at 1. Therefore, the slave has $J = 0$, $K = 1$ and switches states to give $Q = 0$, $\bar{Q} = 1$. Thus the slave is reset by the trailing edge of the clock pulse. Lastly, consider that $J = K = 1$. Since the circuit is set $\bar{Q} = 0$ and one of the three inputs to the upper input AND gate is 0, hence the J input of the master is also 0. The lower input gate now has all three inputs at 1 when a clock pulse arrives and so the master has $K = 1$. This means that the operation when $J = K = 1$ is the same as for the condition $J = 0$, $K = 1$ just described.

Consider now the circuit operation when the flip-flop is initially reset, i.e. $Q = 0$, $\bar{Q} = 1$. When $J = 1$, $K = 0$, the J input of the master will become 1 once a clock pulse is present but the K input will be at 0. Hence $Q' = 1$, $\bar{Q}' = 0$ but state of Q' cannot be passed on to the slave's J input because the inverted clock pulse inhibits the slave input AND gates. When the clock changes from 1 to 0, the J input of the slave will become logic 1 and the slave will be set to have $Q = 1$, $\bar{Q} = 0$. The input state $J = 0$, $K = 1$ will not initiate switching since for this condition neither gate will have all its three inputs at 1.

Master-slave J-K flip-flops are readily available in the TTL, ECL and CMOS families. Figure 6.9 shows the pin conections of the 7476, a TTL circuit providing dual J-K master-slave flip-flops with preset and clear. The *preset* and *clear* terminals, when low, set, or reset, the flip-flop whatever the logic states of the other inputs.

When the preset and the clear inputs are at logic 1, the clock at 1 will enable the J and K inputs and allow data to be inputted. Input data is transferred to the output when the clock changes from 1 to 0.

Other J-K master-slave flip-flops, for example the 7473, are not provided with a preset terminal.

Edge-triggered J-K Flip-flops

As an alternative to the use of the master-slave principle a J-K flip-flop can be *edge-triggered*. With a flip-flop of this type, changes in

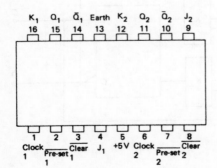

Fig. 6.9 Pin connections of 7476 dual J-K master-slave flip-flop

the output state are initiated by *changes* in the clock pulses. Any change in the input signal that should occur while the clock is steady at logical 1 will not affect the output of the circuit. Circuit operation may be initiated by either *leading-edge* or *trailing-edge* triggering depending on the flip-flop. Most LS flip-flops are trailing-edge triggered. The input signals are not read until the start of the negative clock transition and the outputs change state (if they are going to) before the transition ends.

The D Flip-flop and the D Latch

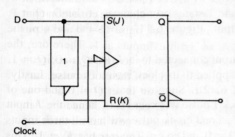

Fig. 6.10 D flip-flop

Table 6.4 D flip-flop

D	Q	Q^+
0	0	0
1	0	1
0	1	0
1	1	1

A D flip-flop has a single trigger (D) input terminal and its logical operation is such that its Q output terminal *always* takes up the same logic value as the D input. Any change in state takes place at instants determined by the clock. The D flip-flop is easily derived from an S-R flip-flop or a J-K flip-flop by connecting an inverting stage between the S and the R, or between the J and the K, terminals as shown by Fig. 6.10. This connection means that always $R = \bar{S}$, or $K = \bar{J}$.

Substituting in the truth table of a J-K flip-flop (or an S-R flip-flop) gives Table 6.4, since when $J = 0$, $K = 1$, and when $J = 1$, $K = 0$. It is clear from Table 6.4 that the Q output of a D flip-flop is always equal to the logical value of its D input.

Integrated circuit versions of the D flip-flop are available in both the TTL and the CMOS families and are of two types.

Some circuits, such as the TTL 7475 and the CMOS 4042, are known as a *latch* and are employed as temporary 1-bit storage devices. Data present at the D input when the clock (enable) is at logic 1 is transferred to the Q output. As long as the clock remains at 1 any changes in the D input state will be followed by the Q output. When the clock goes to logic 0 the Q output will retain its state just prior to the clock change and will not respond to any further changes at the D input. The pin connections of the 7475 are shown by Fig. 6.11a.

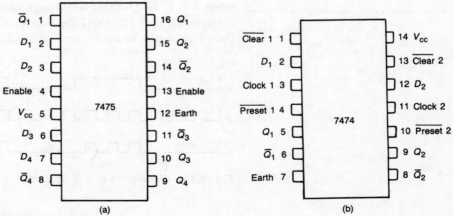

Fig. 6.11 Pin connection of the (*a*) 7475 D latch, (*b*) 7474 D flip-flop

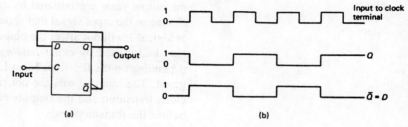

Fig. 6.12 Use of a D flip-flop to divide by two

With a positive edge-triggered D flip-flop, such as the TTL 7474 or the hCMOS HC74, data present at the D input is transferred to the Q output at the leading edge of a clock pulse. When the clock is at either the logic 0 or logic 1 states any changes at the D input have no effect on the Q output. Figure 6.11b gives the 7474 pin connections.

If a D flip-flop has its $\bar{Q}$ output connected to its D input, the circuit will divide by two the signal applied to its clock input. The necessary connection is shown in Fig. 6.12a. Suppose that initially $Q = 1$, $\bar{Q} = D = 0$, then the first clock 1 pulse will cause the circuit to switch to $Q = 0$, $\bar{Q} = D = 1$. The second clock pulse will now switch the circuit back to $Q = 1$, $\bar{Q} = D = 0$ and so on. The circuit waveforms are given by Fig. 6.12b from which it is clear that the output pulse waveform has a frequency of one-half that of the input waveform.

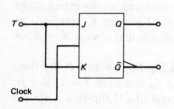

Fig. 6.13 T flip-flop

The T Flip-flop

Table 6.5

J	K	Q	Q^+
0	0	0	0
0	0	1	1
1	1	0	1
1	1	1	0

The fourth type of flip-flop is called the trigger or T flip-flop and its symbol is given by Fig. 6.13. The flip-flop is made from a J-K flip-flop merely by connecting its J and K terminals together. This means that, at all times, $J = K$. Substituting in the truth table of a J-K flip-flop gives Table 6.5. From this table it is apparent that, when the clock is 1, the flip-flop will change state, or **toggle**, each time there is a trigger (T) pulse applied to its input. Thus, when $T = 0$, the Q output will not change state when the clock goes to logic 1; when $T = 1$, the Q output will change state each time a clock pulse is received (Fig. 6.14). The T flip-flop is not available as an integrated circuit since it is so easily obtained from a J-K flip-flop.

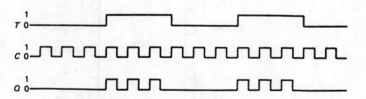

Fig. 6.14 Waveforms in a T flip-flop

7 Counters and Shift Registers

A **counter** is an electronic circuit that is able to count the number of pulses applied to its input terminals. The count may be outputted using the straightforward binary code, or may be in binary-coded decimal (BCD). Alternatively, the outputs of a counter may be decoded to produce a unique output signal to represent each possible count. A counter may also be used as a frequency divider, in which case only one output terminal is required.

Essentially, a counter consists of the cascade connection of a number of flip-flops, usually of either the J-K type or the D type which may be operated either synchronously or non-synchronously. With **synchronous operation** all the flip-flops making up the counter operate at the same instant in time under the control of a clock pulse. In the case of **non-synchronous operation** each flip-flop operates in turn. The switching of the least significant flip-flop is initiated by a clock pulse but the remaining flip-flops are each operated by the preceding flip-flop. This means that each stage must change state before the following stage can do so. As a result synchronous operation of a counter is much faster and the use of a non-synchronous counter is only acceptable when the speed of operation is not of particular importance. On the other hand, a synchronous counter is more complex and so is more expensive.

A counter can be constructed by suitably interconnecting a number of integrated circuit J-K or D flip-flops and, perhaps, gates, but more conveniently several different types of counter are available in integrated circuit form and in this chapter examples will be given of the use of TTL counters.

The possible applications for counters are many. They are often used for the direct counting of objects in industrial processes and of voltage pulses in digital circuits such as digital voltmeters. Counters can be used as frequency dividers and for the measurement of frequency and time.

Non-synchronous Counters

A single J-K flip-flop will act as a divide-by-two circuit. If its J and K terminals are both held at logic 1 and a clock pulse is applied to its clock input terminal, the flip-flop will toggle and so the Q output

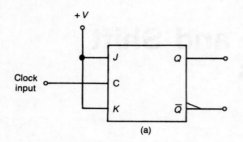

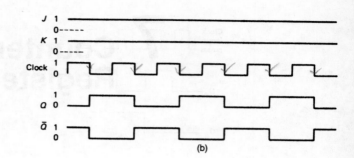

Fig. 7.1 (a) J-K flip-flop ÷ 2, (b) waveforms in a divide-by-two circuit

Table 7.1 4-bit counter

Clock pulse (count)	0	1	2	3	4	5	6	7	8	9	10	11	12	13	14	15	16
Q_A	0	1	0	1	0	1	0	1	0	1	0	1	0	1	0	1	0
Q_B	0	0	1	1	0	0	1	1	0	0	1	1	0	0	1	1	0
Q_C	0	0	0	0	1	1	1	1	0	0	0	0	1	1	1	1	0
Q_D	0	0	0	0	0	0	0	0	1	1	1	1	1	1	1	1	0

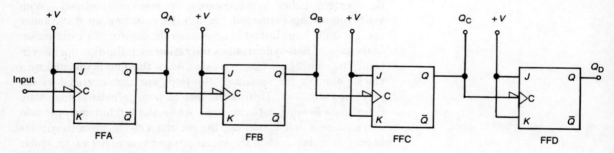

Fig. 7.2 Non-synchronous counter

will switch backwards and forwards between logic 1 and logic 0 (Fig. 7.1). In the drawing of the waveforms shown in Fig. 7.1b it has been assumed that the flip-flop toggles at the trailing edge of the clock pulse, i.e. as the clock pulse changes from 1 to 0. This is generally true for non-synchronous counters. Clearly the number of pulses per second occurring at the Q terminal is only one-half of the number of clock pulses. For counts in excess of two, a number n of J-K flip-flops must be connected in cascade to give a count of $2^n - 1$. Since the first state is 0 this means that n flip-flops are able to give 2^n count states (see Table 7.1). The *count modulus* is 2^n.

Figure 7.2 shows how a non-synchronous counter can be constructed from four J-K flip-flops. The J and the K inputs of each flip-flop are permanently connected to the logic 1 voltage level so that each flip-flop will be toggled by a pulse applied to its clock input. This will NOT be shown in following diagrams. The Q output of the first,

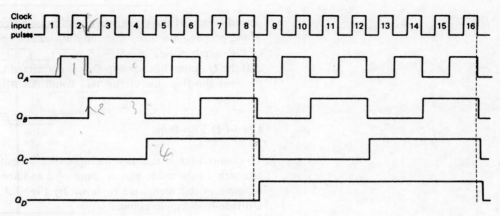

Fig. 7.3 Waveforms in a 4-bit non-synchronous counter

second and third stages is connected to the clock input of the following stage. The $\bar{Q}$ terminals are left unconnected. Each J-K flip-flop is switched by the trailing edge of a pulse applied to its clock input.

Suppose that initially each stage is reset, i.e. $Q_A = Q_B = Q_C = Q_D = 0$. The trailing edge of the first clock pulse will toggle flip-flop A so that Q_A becomes logic 1. The count will then be 0 0 0 1 (reading from the right) or denary 1. The next clock pulse will toggle flip-flop A and the change of Q_A from 1 to 0 will set flip-flop B. Thus, after two clock pulses have been applied to the counter, only Q_B is at 1. The third clock pulse will set flip-flop A so that Q_A changes from 0 to 1 but such a change will not affect the state of flip-flop B and so this stage remains set. Now both the first two stages are set, $Q_A = Q_B = 1$, and the last two stages remain reset, $Q_C = Q_D = 0$; the count is now 0 0 1 1 or decimal 3. When the fourth clock pulse arrives, the first stage toggles so that Q_A changes from 1 to 0, and this change causes flip-flop B to reset. Thus Q_B changes from 1 to 0 and in so doing sets flip-flop C; now $Q_A = Q_B = Q_D = 0$ and $Q_C = 1$ and decimal 4 is stored. The operation of the counter as the fifth, sixth, seventh, etc. clock pulses are applied follows the same lines as just described and is summarized by the truth table of the counter (see Table 7.1). Note that the count is 15 and there are 16 different combinations of Q_A, Q_B, Q_C and Q_D.

The operation of the counter can be illustrated by the waveforms given in Fig. 7.3. The Q outputs of the flip-flops seem to *ripple* through the circuit and for this reason this type of circuit is often known as a **ripple counter**. Since 16 input pulses produce one output pulse the circuit is known as a divide-by-16 counter.

The count is of a binary nature and the counter operates non-synchronously because the flip-flops operate at different times, shown at the end of the eighth and the sixteenth clock pulses by the vertical dotted lines. Flip-flop A operates twice as often as flip-flop B, four times as often as flip-flop C, and eight times as often as flip-flop D. There is a maximum clock frequency that can be used since the periodic time of the clock waveform must be greater than the sum of the propagation times through the counter and the time duration of the output pulse.

If the $\bar{Q}$ output of each flip-flop is connected to the clock input of the next flip-flop, the circuit will count down from 15 to 0.

Use of D Flip-flops

To obtain a count that is a multiple of 2 a number of D flip-flops are each connected to give a count of 2 and are then cascaded. An example of this technique is shown by Fig. 7.4; this set-up acts as a divide-by-8 ripple counter.

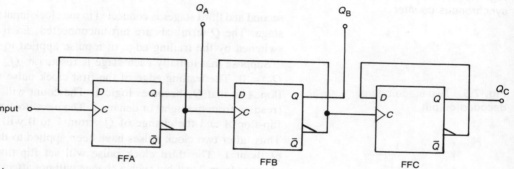

Fig. 7.4 Ripple counter using D flip-flops

Decoded Outputs

Often a binary readout of the count is undesirable; when this is so the outputs of the individual flip-flops of the counter can be **decoded** so that each count produces a unique output. Decoding can be achieved by connecting the Q and the $\bar{Q}$ outputs of each flip-flop to the inputs of a number of gates. This is shown by Fig. 7.5 for a 2-stage counter. The output of a 2-input AND gate is 1 only when both its inputs are at 1. Hence the top gate, for example, will only have an output of logic 1 when $Q_A = Q_B = 1$ and the count is 3.

It is possible for false 1 signals to appear at the flip-flop outputs which may give false counts when decoding circuitry is used. These *glitches* or *dynamic hazards* arise because not all the flip-flops change state at precisely the same time when the edge of a clock pulse arrives. To prevent this happening the decoding gates can be clocked as shown by Fig. 7.6. The enabling clock pulse is not applied until all the flip-flops have reached their steady (final) values. The glitch-free output is, however, obtained at the expense of a reduction in the speed of operation. Some integrated circuit counters include the decoding circuitry within the package.

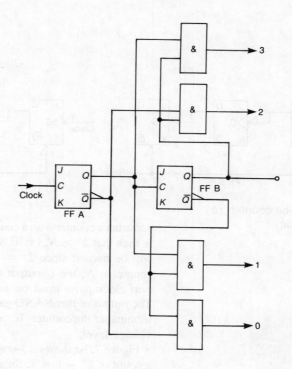

Fig. 7.5 Two-stage counter with decoded output

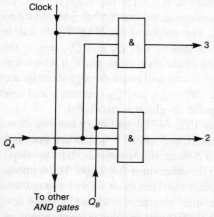

Fig. 7.6 Clocking of decoding gates in a counter

Reducing the Count to Less than 2^n

Very often a counter is required to have a count of less than $2^n - 1$, where n is the number of flip-flops it contains. The reduced count is obtained by modifying the basic counter circuit so that one or more of the possible states are omitted. Thus, if a count of 7 is required, a three-stage counter must be used, having 2^3 or 8 (including 0) states. This means that *one* of the counts must be eliminated. There are three different ways in which one or more counts can be eliminated: (*a*) the feedback method, (*b*) the reset method, and (*c*) the preset method. Most MSI counters employ the reset method and only this is considered here.

The feedback method of reducing the count of a counter consists of feeding back the output(s) Q and/or $\overline{Q}$ of one or more flip-flops to one or more of the preceding flip-flops via suitable gating in order to set or reset them out of their normal $2^n - 1$ count sequence. The feedback method is easily applied to counters made up of separate J-K flip-flops but it cannot be applied to an integrated circuit counter because these devices do not have their internal flip-flop J and K terminals available at the package pins.

Medium-scale integration (MSI) counts can have their count reduced by resetting the circuit at the appropriate point in the counting sequence. The only requirement is that some means of resetting, or clearing, all the flip-flops simultaneously should be provided. To

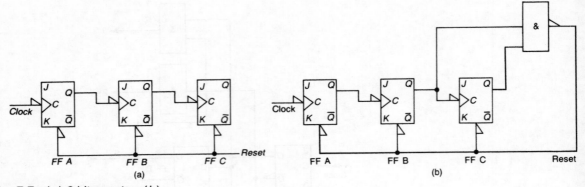

Fig. 7.7 (a) 3-bit counter, (b) divide-by-6 circuit

construct a counter with a count of N, the number n of flip-flops needed is such that $2^n \geq N$, i.e. if $N = 9$ (a decade counter), four flip-flops will be needed since $2^n = 16$. When the count of the unmodified counter is N, the Q output of each flip-flop that will be set on the *next* clock pulse must be connected to the input of a NAND gate. The output of this NAND gate should then be connected to the reset terminal of the counter. IC counters are normally reset by the logic 0 voltage level.

Figure 7.7a shows a 3-stage ripple counter (a $\div 8$ counter) having a count of $2^3 - 1 = 7$. Suppose that this counter is to be converted to have a count of 5. When the count is 6 the flip-flops B and C are set and hence their Q outputs are connected to a NAND gate and thence to the reset line (Fig. 7.7b). The output of the NAND gate will be logic 0 only when both of its inputs, i.e. Q_B and Q_C, are 1; this condition will occur at the end of the sixth clock pulse at which time the counter is reset. Hence the circuit will count through the sequence 0, 1, 2, 3, 4, 5, 0, 1, 2, etc. When Q_B and Q_C become 1 and reset the counter a short output pulse or glitch is produced.

As an example consider the TTL 7493 4-bit binary counter shown in Fig. 7.8. It can be seen that flip-flops B, C and D are internally connected together to form a 3-stage ripple counter, but flip-flop A is not internally connected to the other three flip-flops. The terminals marked R_{01} and R_{02} are the 'reset-to-0' inputs. A logic 1 voltage level applied to both of these terminals produces a logic 0 voltage level at the output of the associated NAND gate and this is the state required to reset, or clear, all four flip-flops (indicated by the small triangle at the clear terminal of each flip-flop). For this integrated circuit to be used as a 0–15 counter, or a *divide-by-16* circuit, pin 12 should be connected to pin 1 to give a 4-stage ripple counter.

The 7493 can be made to have a count, or a division ratio, of less than 16 by use of the R_{01} and R_{02} input terminals. To obtain a **decade counter** pin 9 should be connected to pin 2; pin 11 should be connected to pin 3; and pin 12 should be connected to pin 1. The circuit is then set up as shown in Fig. 7.9. When the count reaches decimal 10, $Q_B = Q_D = 1$ and the output of the NAND gate becomes 0,

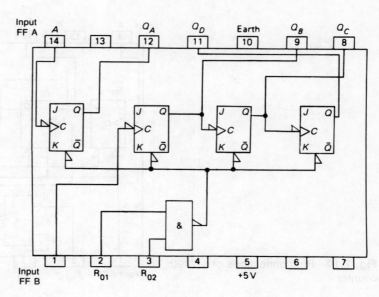

Fig. 7.8 7493 4-bit binary counter

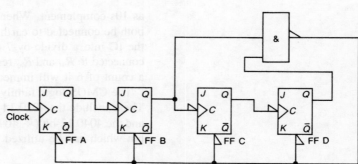

Fig. 7.9 7493 connected as a decade counter

resetting all four flip-flops. To obtain a divide-by-11 counter connect Q_D to R_{02}, and Q_A and Q_B to a NAND gate whose output is connected to R_{01}.

The TTL 7490 is a decade counter that consists of one J-K flip-flop which acts as a divide-by-two circuit and a 3-stage counter that is internally connected to give a count of 5. The pin connections of the 7490 are shown in Fig. 7.10. To obtain the maximum count pin 12 must be connected externally to pin 1. The overall division ratio is thus $2 \times 5 = 10$ but the mark/space ratio is 1:4. If the $\div 5$ circuit is placed first and followed by the $\div 2$ circuit an alternative decade counter is obtained. The output is now taken from Q_A and the count follows the sequence 0, 1, 2, 3, 4, 8, 9, 10, 11, and 12. This connection has the merit that its output waveform is square. In addition to the clear or reset terminals marked R_{01} and R_{02}, this particular integrated circuit has two other pins, labelled as R_{91} and R_{92}, which can be used to set the counter to a count of 9.

The R_{91} and R_{92} pins are used in a form of BCD subtraction known

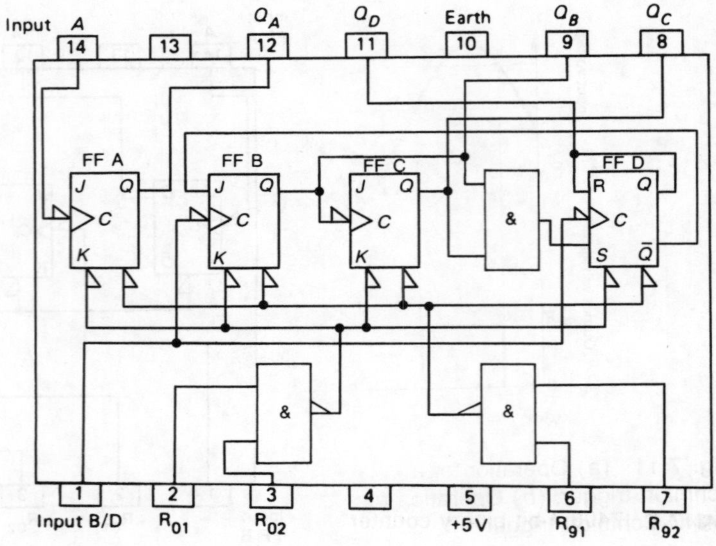

Fig. 7.10 Pin connections of a 7490 counter

as 10s complement. When these two pins are not used they should both be connected to earth. They can, however, be used to convert the IC into a divide-by-7 counter. The output pins Q_B and Q_C are connected to R_{91} and R_{92} respectively. Then, when the circuit reaches a count of 6 it will immediately move to a count of 9.

The CMOS logic family also offers a number of ripple counters. These include the 4020 14-bit ($\div$ 16 384), the 4024 7-bit ($\div$ 128), and the 4040 12-bit ($\div$ 4096) ICs. These three ICs have a reset input pin which can be utilized to modify their count.

Clocks

Most digital circuits use some form of rectangular pulse generator, known as the *clock*, to control the times at which the various stages change state. At lower frequencies the clock may consist of an astable multivibrator or a Schmidtt trigger oscillator but at higher frequencies the clock is usually some form of crystal oscillator in order to achieve good frequency stability.

Schmidtt Trigger

A **Schmidtt trigger** is a circuit, readily available as an integrated circuit, whose output voltage can have only one of two possible values. The output voltage will be high, +3.3 V for a TTL version, when the input is greater than a positive-going *threshold voltage*, and will remain at this value until such time as the input voltage falls below the negative-going threshold voltage. The operation of a Schmidtt trigger circuit is shown by Fig. 7.11a; when the input sinusoidal voltage becomes more positive than the positive threshold voltage, the output of the circuit switches to become +3.3 V. The output

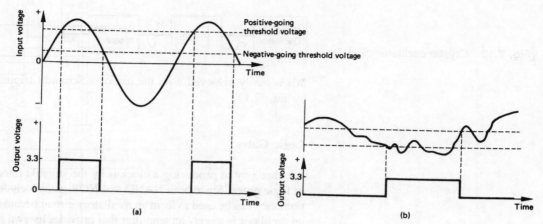

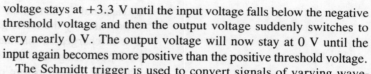

Fig. 7.11 (*a*) Operation of a Schmidtt trigger, (*b*) Operation of a NAND Schmidtt trigger

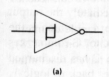

(a)

(b)

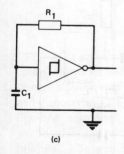

(c)

Fig. 7.12 Symbols for (*a*) Schmidtt trigger, (*b*) NAND Schmidtt trigger. (*c*) Use of a Schmidtt trigger as a clock oscillator

voltage stays at +3.3 V until the input voltage falls below the negative threshold voltage and then the output voltage suddenly switches to very nearly 0 V. The output voltage will now stay at 0 V until the input again becomes more positive than the positive threshold voltage.

The Schmidtt trigger is used to convert signals of varying wave-shapes into rectangular pulses of short rise time and fall time. Some IC Schmidtt triggers are associated with 2-input or 4-input NAND gates; the gates allow the trigger to be enabled by the signals applied to the gates. Essentially a NAND Schmidtt trigger consists of a NAND gate followed by a Schmidtt trigger. The input to the trigger will be at a high voltage only when all the inputs to the NAND gate are low. This means that the operation is the inverse of that of the basic trigger. Suppose, for example, that the waveform shown in Fig. 7.11*b* is applied to the commoned inputs of a 2-input or a 4-input NAND Schmidtt trigger. The output of the circuit will be at zero volts until the input voltage first reaches the lower threshold voltage. When this point is reached, all the NAND inputs are low and so its output is high, causing the trigger output to rise to +3.3 V. The output will remain at +3.3 V until the input voltage rises to some value more positive than the input upper threshold voltage, and then it will abruptly switch to zero volts.

The symbols for a Schmidtt trigger and a NAND Schmidtt trigger are shown in Figs 7.12*a* and *b* respectively. Also shown in Fig. 7.12*c* is a diagram of how a Schmidtt trigger can be used as a clock oscillator. Note that the Schmidtt trigger symbol indicates that its output is inverted, i.e. the output is low even when the input is high. This is true for the ttl version of the circuit — the 7414.

Crystal Oscillator

When a **crystal oscillator** is used as the clock, it is necessary to convert its sinusoidal output voltage into the required rectangular waveform;

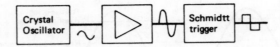

Fig. 7.13 Crystal oscillator clock

this is easily achieved with the use of a Schmidtt trigger as shown by Fig. 7.13.

Logic Gates

Another way of producing a clock is by the suitable interconnection of **logic gates**. Since both NAND and NOR gates include amplification, they can be used to form an oscillatory circuit because essentially an oscillator is merely an amplifier that provides its own input signal. One way in which NOR and NAND gates can be connected to form a clock is shown in Fig. 7.14a. The feedback network is provided by capacitor C and resistor R together with NOR gate B. The amplifier is provided by the NOR gate A. Suppose that initially the capacitor C is discharged so that the clock output is zero. The gate B inverts its input voltage and so its output voltage is at the logic 1 level. Capacitor C is therefore charged via R with a time constant of CR seconds. As C charges, the voltage across it rises until it becomes equal to the value corresponding to logic 1. Immediately the output of gate B goes to logic 0 and so the output of gate A — which is the required clock output — goes to logic 1. Now capacitor C commences to discharge via R to the output of gate B. Once C has discharged to the level at which the output of gate B switches back to logic 1, the output of gate A goes to logic 0. The frequency of operation of the clock is determined by the time constant CR.

An alternative method of making a clock from NOR or NAND gates is given by Fig. 7.14b.

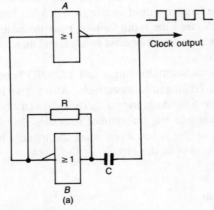

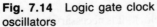

(a)

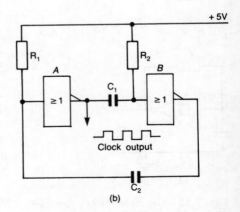

Fig. 7.14 Logic gate clock oscillators

Synchronous Counters

A ripple counter can only be used for applications in which the speed of operation is not very important. If several stages of counting are employed, the time taken for a clock pulse to *ripple* through the counter may well be excessive. The operating time can be shortened considerably and glitches avoided by arranging for all the flip-flops to be clocked at the same moment. This is known as *synchronous* operation.

In a synchronous counter all the flip-flops change their state simultaneously, the operation of each stage being initiated by the clock. The arrangement of a 4-bit synchronous counter is shown in Fig. 7.15. The clock input of each flip-flop is directly connected to the clock line so that they all operate simultaneously. The Q output of the first stage is connected to the commoned J and K inputs of the second stage, but the third and the fourth stages have their input state determined by the Q outputs of *all* the previous stages.

The operation of the *divide-by-16* synchronous counter is as follows. Suppose that initially all the four stages are reset so that the count is 0, i.e. $Q_A = Q_B = Q_C = Q_D = 0$. At the trailing edge of the first clock pulse, flip-flop A toggles so that $Q_A = 1$. The second stage now has $J_B = K_B = 1$ and so it will toggle when the second clock pulse ends and Q_A changes from 1 to 0. Now $Q_A = 0$ and $Q_B = 1$. AND gate A now has one input at 1 and the other input at 0 and so flip-flop C has $J_C = K_C = 0$ and will *not* toggle at the end of the next clock pulse. When the third clock pulse ends, flip-flop A toggles, Q_A changes from 0 to 1, and flip-flop B remains set. Now $Q_A = Q_B = 1$, so the count is 3, and both inputs to gate A are at logic 1. This means that flip-flop C has $J_C = K_C = 1$ and will toggle when the fourth clock pulse ends. Thus, the fourth clock pulse resets flip-flops A and B and sets flip-flop C; now only $Q_C = 1$ and the count is 4. The operation of the counter continues in this way as further clock pulses are applied. All three inputs to AND gate B will be at 1 after the *seventh* clock pulse has ended and $Q_A = Q_B = Q_C = 1$.

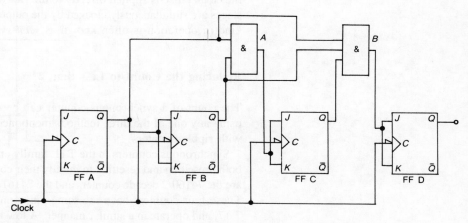

Fig. 7.15 Synchronous counter

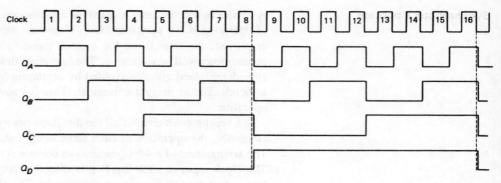

Fig. 7.16 Waveforms in a 4-bit synchronous counter

Thus flip-flop D will toggle to be set at the trailing edge of the eighth pulse.

The operation of the counter as 16 clock pulses are applied is summarized by the timing diagram given in Fig. 7.16. In this figure the vertical dotted lines indicate the time delay that occurs between the clock pulse changing from 1 to 0 and the flip-flops toggling. Note that there is one output (Q_D) pulse for 16 input (clock) pulses.

The synchronous counter is faster to operate than the non-synchronous counter because the clock frequency is only limited by the delay of *one* flip-flop (since all flip-flops operate simultaneously) plus the delays introduced by the AND gates. Other advantages are: (i) a decoded synchronous counter does not usually suffer from glitches, and (ii) since all flip-flops change state simultaneously, a binary (or BCD) output cannot be misread.

Many integrated circuit synchronous counters operate at the leading edge of the clock pulses and not at the trailing edge as was shown by Fig. 7.16. This may sometimes be an advantage when a counter is interfaced with other digital circuitry. In some integrated counters the first and the second stages are not internally coupled together; the clock pulse is applied directly to the first stage and the remaining stages are simultaneously clocked by the output of the first stage. This kind of operation is often known as *semi-synchronous*.

Reducing the Count to Less than 2^n

The count of a synchronous counter can be reduced to less than 2^n using any one of the three methods mentioned earlier in conjunction with ripple counters.

Synchronous counters in the TTL family employ a combination of both presetting and resetting to modify their count. Four such counters are the 74160/2 decade counters and the 74161/3 4-bit binary counters. These four counters have the same pin connections, shown in Fig. 7.17, and operate in a similar manner. A low level applied to the reset terminal will reset all four stages at the leading edge of the next clock

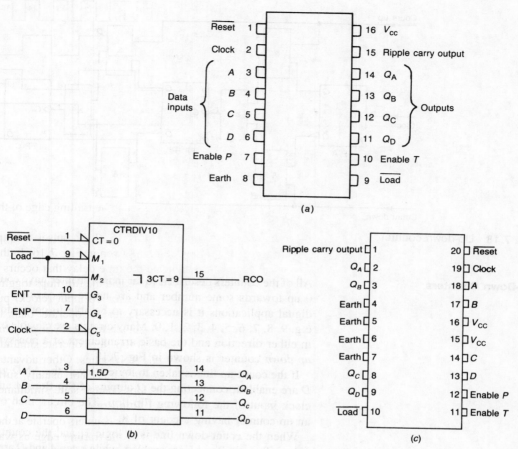

Fig. 7.17 (a) Pin connections and (b) logic symbol of the 74160 counter; (c) pin connections of the AC/ACT 160

pulse. The load terminal is then taken low to disable the counter. The data present at the data inputs A, B, C and D then either resets or presets each flip-flop. This step presets the count to a desired figure.

The load input terminal is then returned to the high state and the two enable inputs P and T are taken high to allow the count to proceed. When the wanted count has been reached the Q outputs of the flip-flops that are then set are connected, via a NAND gate, to the reset pin to return the count to the preset figure.

Synchronous counters in the CMOS 4000 family include the 4518 decade counter and the 4520 divide-by-16 counter. Most CMOS counters employ a different technique and are known as Johnson counters. 74HC and 74HCT counters have the same pin connections while the pin connections for the AC160/1/2/3 and ACT160/1/2/3 counters are shown in Fig. 7.17(c).

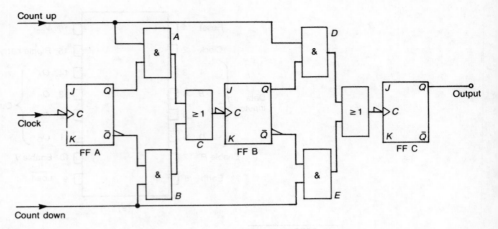

Fig. 7.18 Up-down counter

Up-Down Counters

All of the counters described so far in this chapter have counted from 0 up towards some number and are hence *up-counters*. For some digital applications it is necessary to be able to count downwards, e.g. 9, 8, 7, 6, 5, 4, 3, 2, 1, 0. Many circuits are capable of counting in either direction and the basic arrangement of a non-synchronous *up-down* counter is shown in Fig. 7.18.

If the count-up line is taken to logic 1 level, the AND gates A and D are enabled, connecting the Q outputs of flip-flops A and B to the clock input of the following flip-flop. The circuit then operates as an up-counter having a count of 8.

When the count-down line is at logic 1, and the count-up line is at logic 0, gates B and E are enabled, while gates A and D are inhibited. Now the $\bar{Q}$ outputs of flip-flops A and B are connected to the clock inputs of the following stages. Suppose that initially all three flip-flops are set, i.e. the count is 7. At the end of the first clock pulse, flip-flop A resets so that $\bar{Q}_A = 1$ and the count is 1 1 0 or 6. The next clock pulse causes flip-flop A to toggle and the trailing edge of its $\bar{Q}$ pulse resets flip-flop B; now the count is 1 0 1 or 5. At the end of the third clock pulse, the first stage toggles so that $Q_A = 0$, $\bar{Q}_A = 1$ and the count is 1 0 0 or 4. The state of the counter is now $\bar{Q}_A = \bar{Q}_B = 1$, $\bar{Q}_C = 0$, and so the fourth clock pulse sets flip-flops A and B and resets flip-flop C to give a count of 3, and so on until all three stages are reset. The count is then 0 and the next clock pulse will return the counter to its original count of 7.

Most integrated circuit up-down counters are of the synchronous type, e.g. TTL, HC, HCT, AC and ACT 190/1/2/3 which are, respectively, BCD, binary, decade, and 4-bit types, and CMOS 4510 BCD and 4516 binary. A BCD counter counts nine pulses in the usual way but when a tenth clock pulse is received resets all four flip-flops and produces a carry 1 bit output for application to the next, higher order, stage.

The relative merits of TTL and CMOS circuits have been tabulated earlier (p. 54). TTL counters can operate at much higher clock frequencies than 4000 CMOS, e.g. standard TTL 20−30 MHz, low-power Schottky TTL 10−100 MHz, CMOS 10 MHz. But HC and AC circuits are as fast as their TTL alternatives.

All versions of CMOS counters dissipate much less power than TTL counters. Another advantage of 4000 CMOS devices is that a much larger number of stages can be provided within a standard d.i.l. IC package. The 4020 has 14 stages and the 4045 has 21 stages, for example. Because of the limitations on the number of package pins, only a few stages (usually one) can have an output that is externally accessible.

The Shift Register

A shift register consists of a number of either D or J-K flip-flops connected in cascade. The number of flip-flops used to form the register is equal to the number of bits to be stored. The flip-flops are generally provided with clear or reset terminals so that the register can be cleared.

A shift register can be operated in any of the four ways:

    (i) serial-in/parallel-out (SIPO)
    (ii) parallel-in/serial-out (PISO)
    (iii) serial-in/serial-out (SISO)
    (iv) parallel-in/parallel-out (PIPO)

shown in Fig. 7.19. The main applications for a shift register are:

(a) the temporary storage of data

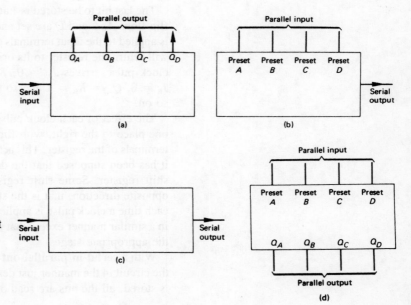

Fig. 7.19 Methods of using a shift register:
(a) serial-in/parallel-out
(b) parallel-in/serial-out
(c) serial-in/serial-out
(d) parallel-in/parallel-out

1011

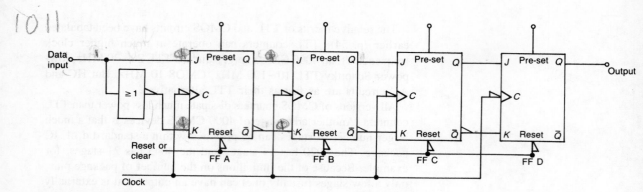

Data input

≥ 1

Reset or clear

Clock

J Pre-set Q

C

K Reset Q̄

FF A

J Pre-set Q

C

K Reset Q̄

FF B

J Pre-set Q

C

K Reset Q̄

FF C

J Pre-set Q

C

K Reset Q̄

FF D

Output

Fig. 7.20 Shift register

(*b*) serial-to-parallel or parallel-to-serial conversion, and
(*c*) digital delay circuits.

The basic arrangement of a shift register is shown in Fig. 7.20.

Suppose that initially all the four flip-flops shown are cleared, i.e. $Q_A = Q_B = Q_C = Q_D = 0$ and that the 4-bit word to be stored is 1011. The first bit is a 1 so that the J and K inputs of FFA are 1 and 0, respectively.

At the end of the first clock pulse, flip-flop A is set so that $Q_A = J_B = 1$, $\bar{Q}_A = K_B = 0$. This is the SET condition for FFB.

After the second clock pulse flip-flop B is also set, and now $Q_A = Q_B = 1$.

The state of the register when the third clock pulse arrives is $J_A = 0$, $K_A = 1$, $J_B = J_C = 1$, $K_B = K_C = 0$ and at the trailing edge of the clock pulse flip-flop A resets and flip-flop C sets. Now $Q_A = J_B = 0$, $Q_B = Q_C = J_C = J_D = 1$.

The last bit to be stored is 1 and at the end of the fourth clock pulse flip-flops A, C and D are set and flip-flop B is reset. If no more data is applied to the input terminals of the register, four more clock pulses will return the register to its original reset condition. When the fifth clock pulse arrives $J_A = 0$, $K_A = 1$ so FFA resets. Now $Q_A = J_B = 0$, $\bar{Q}_A = K_B = 1$ and so the sixth clock pulse resets FFB and so on.

The effect of each clock pulse is to shift the content of each stage one place to the right, with flip-flop A storing the data at the input terminals of the register. This action is illustrated by Fig. 7.21 in which it has been supposed that the data 1101 has been fed into a 6-stage shift register. Some shift registers are arranged to operate in the opposite direction, that is the stored data shifts one place to the left each time a clock pulse is applied. The other types of register operate in a similar manner except that parallel loading is achieved by setting the appropriate stages.

With a **serial-in/parallel-out** register (Fig. 7.19*a*) data is fed into the circuit in the manner just described and, when the complete word is stored, all the bits are read off simultaneously from the output of

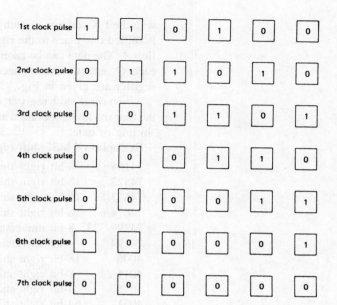

1st clock pulse	1	1	0	1	0	0
2nd clock pulse	0	1	1	0	1	0
3rd clock pulse	0	0	1	1	0	1
4th clock pulse	0	0	0	1	1	0
5th clock pulse	0	0	0	0	1	1
6th clock pulse	0	0	0	0	0	1
7th clock pulse	0	0	0	0	0	0

Fig. 7.21 Movement of data through a shift register

each stage. The register acts to convert data from serial form into parallel form and it is sometimes employed as a data buffer.

The **parallel-in/serial-out** register (Fig. 7.19b) operates in exactly the opposite way. The data to be stored is set up by first clearing all the stages and then applying a 1 to the preset terminal of each flip-flop which is to be set. The data is read out of the register, one bit at a time, under the control of the clock. The circuit is employed to convert data from parallel to serial form.

The **serial-in/serial-out** register (Fig. 7.19c) can be used as a delay circuit or as a temporary store but the stored data can only be accessed in the order in which it was stored.

Figure 7.19d shows a **parallel-in/parallel-out** register and this also acts as a short-term store.

A shift register that uses D flip-flops is shown by Fig. 7.22. As

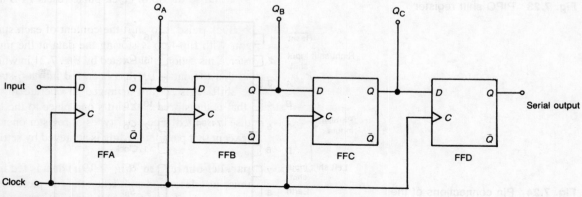

Fig. 7.22 D flip-flop shift register

with the J-K version, at each clock pulse the data held in the register is shifted one place to the right and data enters from the left at flip-flop A. The data can be taken off serially via Q_D or in parallel from each Q output. The connections required for a D flip-flop PIPO register are given in Fig. 7.23.

A *universal* shift register is one that can be employed in any of the four modes of operation and is also capable of both left- and right-shifting of data.

Examples of MSI shift registers are:

74164	8-bit right-shift SIPO
74322	8-bit right-shift all 4 modes
74673/5	16-bit right-shift SIPO and SISO
74674/6	16-bit right-shift SISO and PISO
74299/323	8-bit universal
74194	4-bit universal
4006	18-bit right-shift SISO
4014/21	8-bit right-shift PISO
4015	4-bit right-shift SIPO
4031	64-bit right-shift SISO
4035	4-bit universal

The pin connections of the 74194 universal shift register are given in Fig. 7.24. To parallel load the circuit the pins S_0 and S_1 are taken

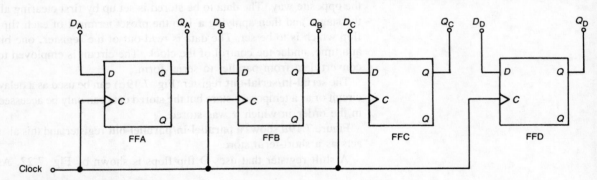

Fig. 7.23 PIPO shift register

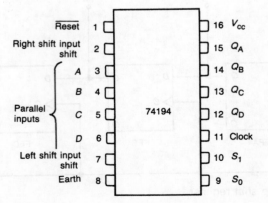

Fig. 7.24 Pin connections of the 74194 universal shift register

high and the input data is applied to the parallel input pins A, B, C and D. Serial loading of data can be achieved via *either* the right serial input shift pin *or* the left serial input pin, depending on whether right- or left-shifting of data is to be selected. The register right-shifts data when pin S_0 is high and pin S_1 is low, and it left-shifts data for the condition $S_0 = 0$, $S_1 = 1$.

8 Semiconductor Memories

Types of Memory

Many digital systems include a **memory** or **store** for the temporary or long-term storage of information. In a digital computer, this information will include numerical data, the intermediate results of computations, and the programs which control the operation of the system. In a telephone exchange, a memory may be used to store code translations and information about each line, such as its number and the nature of the equipment connected to it. A memory should have sufficient capacity to be able to satisfy all the demands made for data and program storage and should be so fast to operate that undue delay is not caused to the main processor. It is also desirable for a memory to be of the minimum possible cost and to be reliable. A long-term memory must allow the stored data to be retained if the power supplies should be shut down. Because of the various demands on a memory a computer employs more than one kind of store.

Hard and/or floppy discs are used for permanent data storage. Semiconductory memories may provide either permanent, or temporary, storage depending upon whether it is a RAM or a ROM. Short-term memory is provided by **registers**.

It must be possible both to write information into a memory and to read information out of the memory. To make this possible a memory consists of a large number of **locations** at each of which one data word can be stored. Each location has a unique **address** so that it can be accessed from outside the memory. The **access time** of a memory is the time that is needed to read one word out of the memory, or to write one word into the memory. The access time of a main store must be measured in nanoseconds and this means that it must be of the random access type. A **random access memory**, or RAM, is one in which any location can be accessed without having to go through all the addresses in sequence. Thus the time taken to read from, or to write into, any location is the same as for any other location. RAMs are either *dynamic* or *static* devices depending upon the way in which data is stored.

The basic requirements of any memory or store are that

(*a*) any required location in the store can be addressed;
(*b*) data can be read out of an addressed location;
(*c*) data can be written into an addressed location (once only in some cases).

If a memory is able to retain the data stored in it when the power supplies have been switched off, the memory is said to be **nonvolatile**. A volatile store will lose the data stored within it if the power supplies are removed.

Semiconductor memories are cheaper, smaller and faster operating than hard or floppy discs. A random access memory (RAM) or read-only memory (ROM) can be formed within a single integrated circuit and made available in a standard dil package.

Read-only memories, or ROMS, are memories into which data is permanently programmed either at the time of manufacture or by the user prior to the memory being installed into an equipment. Essentially a ROM consists of a matrix of conductors, some of whose intersections are linked by diodes or transistors.

A RAM consists of a matrix of memory cells together with digital circuits that provide such functions as *address selection* and *control*. Each memory cell can hold one bit of information and is situated at a matrix location that is identified by a unique address that has two parts, a row select signal and a column select signal.

The capacity of a semiconductor memory is the number of bits of information it is able to store and this is usually quoted in *kilobits*. The prefix kilo does not stand for 1000, as is usual in most other contexts, but, instead, it stands for 2^{10} or 1024. Memory ICs are manufactured in various sizes that are always some power-of-2 multiple of kilobits, such as 16k, 32k, 64k, and so on. Thus, a 16k memory has a capacity of 16×1024 or 16 384 bits, and a 64k memory has a capacity of 65 536 bits.

The *organization* of a semiconductor memory is the manner in which the memory cell(s) at each addressable location are arranged. Each of the addressable locations will contain a digital *word* that may consist of only 1 bit, or it may consist of either 4 or 8 bits. The organization of a memory is quoted by its manufacturer in the form *m* locations $\times$ *n* bits per location. For example, a 64k memory could be organized as $64k \times 1$, $16k \times 4$ or $8k \times 8$. The $64k \times 1$ memory has 64k addressable locations at each of which is stored a 1-bit word. The $16k \times 4$ memory holds 16k 4-bit words, and the $8k \times 8$ memory contains 8k 8-bit words.

Memory locations are addressed using binary numbering and *address decoders* since this reduces the number of package pins that are necessary. If there are *n* address pins, then 2^n different memory locations can be addressed. This means that a $16k \times 1$ memory requires 13 address pins (labelled A_0, A_1, through to A_{12}) and 1 data pin; an $8k \times 8$ memory has 12 address pins and 8 data pins and so on, see Fig. 8.3.

EXAMPLE 8.1

Calculate the number of locations that may be addressed in a RAM that has (a) 10 address pins, and (b) 16 address pins.

Solution
(a) $2^{10} = 1024 = 1 \text{ k}$. (*Ans*)
(b) $2^{16} = 65536 = 64 \text{ k}$. (*Ans*)

Random Access Memories

The matrix of a **random access memory** or **RAM** is organized as m words of n bits each, i.e. $m \times n$. The memory cells are located at the intersections of the m rows and the n columns of the matrix. The idea is illustrated by Fig. 8.1a which shows a square matrix in which $m = n = 5$. This is not a size used in practice but has been drawn for simplicity. Each location is given a unique address so that any location can be selected at a time.

To reduce the number of column and row address lines needed, addresses are signalled using the binary code and are decoded to produce voltages on the selected column and row lines. The arrangement used is shown in Fig. 8.1b for a $1k \times 1$ memory. Suppose, for example, that the memory cell located at the intersection of row 2 and column 13 is to be selected. Then the input to the row decoder must be 00010 and the input to the column decoder must be 01101.

The diagram also shows a block marked as control. This circuit performs the functions either of writing new data into an addressed location, or of reading out existing data. The read/$\overline{\text{write}}$ input determines which of the two functions is performed. The chip select $\overline{\text{CS}}$ input must (usually) be low to enable the memory; this facility is used when two or more chips are combined to produce a larger capacity

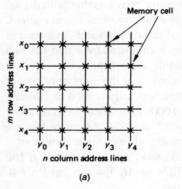

(a)

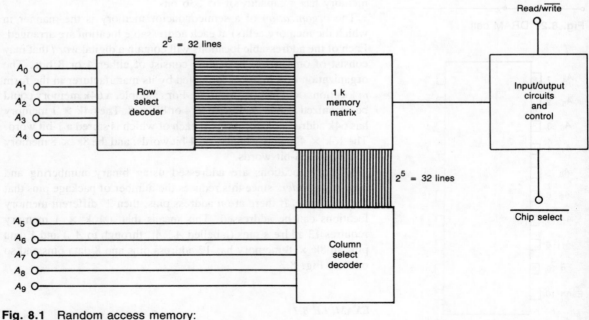

(b)

Fig. 8.1 Random access memory: (a) memory matrix, (b) block diagram

memory. When the $\overline{CS}$ pin is high the device has a high output impedance.

When the data stored at a location is to be read, the read/$\overline{write}$ line is set to the logic 1 voltage level, and the address of the required location is fed into the address decoders. The data held at that location then appears at the data-out terminal(s). The read-out process is *non-destructive*.

When new data is to be written into the memory, the read/$\overline{write}$ line is set to the logic 0 voltage level. The data present at the data-in terminal(s) will then be written into the addressed memory cell(s).

Two kinds of RAM are manufactured, known respectively as the static RAM and the dynamic RAM. In a **static RAM** (SRAM) the memory cells are actually flip-flops that can be fabricated using either bipolar transistor, NMOS or CMOS technology. Examples of static RAMs in the TTL family are the 74301 256 × 1 and the N8 350 256 × 8, the former having an open-circuit output and the latter having a three-state output. CMOS static RAMs are of larger capacity, such as 4k × 1, 16k × 1 or 16k ×4 and dissipate less power than the bipolar transistor versions but, on the other hand, they have greater access times. RAMs are volatile.

A **dynamic RAM** (DRAM) does not use flip-flops as the memory cells but, instead, data is stored in the stray capacitances that inevitably exist between the gate and the source of a mosfet. The principle of a DRAM memory cell is shown by Fig. 8.2. For data to be written into the cell switch S_1 is closed and switch S_2 is open. The capacitance C is then either charged up to a relatively high voltage if the input data is binary 1, or it is discharged to very nearly zero volts if the input data is binary 0. To read out the data held in the cell S_1 is opened and S_2 is closed so that the voltage across the capacitance appears at the output of the cell. The charge stored in the capacitance leaks away with time and so each cell in a DRAM must be *refreshed* at regular intervals of about 2 ms. The refreshing process is carried out by first reading the data from a cell and then writing it back into the cell. The dynamic RAM has the advantages that (i) a larger storage capacity can be provided within a given chip area, (ii) it is faster to operate and is cheaper to fabricate than a static RAM. On the other hand, the dynamic RAM possesses the disadvantage of needing periodic *refreshing* of the stored data.

Dynamic RAMs can only be provided using mosfet technology, and development in this field is extremely rapid. Presently available are 16k × 1, 64k × 1, 16k × 4, 256k × 1, 1M × 1 and 4M × 1 devices.

The pin connections of a typical static 4k × 4 RAM are given in Fig. 8.2. There are 12 address pins, labelled A_0, A_1, through to A_{11}, giving 2^{12} addressable memory locations; 4 data input/output pins to give 4-bit words at each address; 2 power supply pins (V_{CC} and earth); 1 chip select pin ($\overline{CS}$) that is active low; and 1 write enable pin (R/$\overline{W}$) which is also active when low.

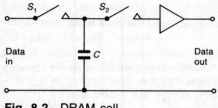

Fig. 8.2   DRAM cell

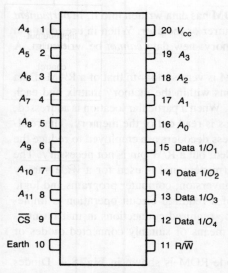

Fig. 8.3   Pin connections of a 4k × 4 RAM

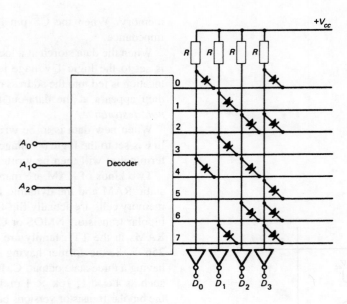

Fig. 8.4 Diode-read only memory

EXAMPLE 8.2

Determine the minimum number of pins for a 16k × 4 RAM.

Solution

16k memory locations require 14 address pins since $2^{14} = 16384$.

There are 4 bits/location and so there are 4 data input/output pins: 1 read/write pin, 1 $\overline{CS}$ pin, 1 power supply voltage pin, 1 earth pin.

Therefore, pins required = 22.   (*Ans*)

Read-only Memories

A **read-only memory** or **ROM** has data written into it, in *permanent form*, by either the manufacturer or the user. When in use, data can *only* be read out of the memory; new data *cannot* be written in. A ROM is non-volatile.

The organization of a ROM is very similar to that of a RAM. Data is stored at different locations within the memory matrix and each location has a unique address. When a particular location is addressed, the data stored at that address is read out of the memory. The read-out is non-destructive. Address decoders are employed to reduce the number of address pins needed, but a R/$\overline{W}$ pin is not necessary. The data held in the ROM is permanent and is used for a wide variety of purposes, such as code conversion, computer programs and logic functions. The truth table of a required circuit operation is implemented by a matrix, with the required connections at matrix intersections being achieved by means of suitably connected diodes or transistors.

The arrangement of a diode ROM is shown in Fig. 8.4. Diodes are connected between some of the row and some of the column lines. When a decoder line, 0 through to 7, is selected and goes low, the associated diodes turn ON. Each output line D_0, D_1, D_2 or D_3 connected to an ON diode is then taken low also. When, for example, the input address is $A_0 = 0$, $A_1 = A_2 = 1$, line 6 goes low and the output of the ROM is $D_0 = D_1 = 1$, $D_2 = D_3 = 0$. Hence,

$$D_0 = \overline{A}\overline{B}\overline{C} + \overline{A}\overline{B}C,$$
$$D_1 = \overline{A}\overline{B}\overline{C} + \overline{A}B\overline{C} + ABC,$$
$$D_2 = \overline{A}B\overline{C} + \overline{A}\overline{B}C + \overline{A}BC,$$
$$D_3 = \overline{A}B\overline{C} + \overline{A}\overline{B}C + A\overline{B}C + \overline{A}BC + ABC$$

A ROM is programmed during manufacture and this data cannot be subsequently altered. This means that the intending user must inform the ROM manufacturer of the particular data that each location is to contain. This is acceptable to the large-scale user but it is much less convenient for the user of much smaller quantities. To provide some flexibility in the possible applications of ROMs, user-programmable devices are often used.

Programmable ROMs

A **programmable read-only memory** or **PROM** is designed so that it can be programmed by the user to meet a specific application for the device. All of the intersections in the memory matrix are linked by a fusible diode or transistor (see Fig. 8.5). When the PROM is purchased from the manufacturer, all of the outputs are at the logic 0 voltage level. The programming procedure consists of changing the bits stored at selected locations from 0 to 1.

Programming of a PROM is accomplished by addressing a particular location in the memory that is to store a 1, and then passing a sufficiently large current through the transistor to blow the fuse. The transistor then no longer links the row and column lines at that location. Once programmed a PROM cannot be reprogrammed.

There are several TTL PROMs available, some examples being 74186 64 × 8, 74199 32 × 8, 74287 254 × 4, and 74470 256 × 8; CMOS devices include HM6641 512 × 8, HM6664 8k × 8 and HM65262 16k × 1.

PROMS are widely used in the control of electrical equipment such as washing machines and ovens.

Erasable and Electrically Alterable PROMs

Some PROMs can have their programs altered and a new program written into the memory. In an **erasable PROM** or **EPROM** the logic 1 state is stored at a location by the storage of an electrical charge and not by the blowing of a fuse. The charge may be held for many years. When a program is to be erased, the chip is exposed to ultraviolet radiation that is directed through a transparent quartz window

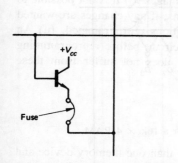

Fig. 8.5 Element in a PROM

in the chip package. This radiation removes the stored charge at *every* location in the memory so that all locations store binary 0. Reprogramming is carried out by addressing each cell that is to store a logic 1 bit and then causing that cell to store a charge.

An alternative to the EPROM is known as the **electrically alterable PROM** or **EAPROM**. Again, programming a memory cell to store logic 1 is accomplished by charging that cell. With the EAPROM, however, the erasure procedure is carried out by applying a reverse-polarity voltage to a cell that removes any stored charge. The EAPROM offers an advantage over the EPROM in that the erasure process can be applied to an individual cell in the matrix and without removal of the IC from the circuit.

The EPROM has two main disadvantages. (i) It is not possible to just reprogram a selected few locations; if any changes are wanted all data must be erased and all locations reprogrammed. (ii) An EPROM must be removed from its circuit before reprogramming can be carried out. The EAPROM does not suffer from these disadvantages.

Memory decoding

Many memory systems include more than one memory device and then some way of selecting a particular IC is necessary. Figure 8.6 shows a system that consists of two RAMs and two ROMs each of which has a capacity of $2^{14} = 16k$ addressable locations. A standard 16-bit address bus is used and the bits A_0 through to A_{13} are used to

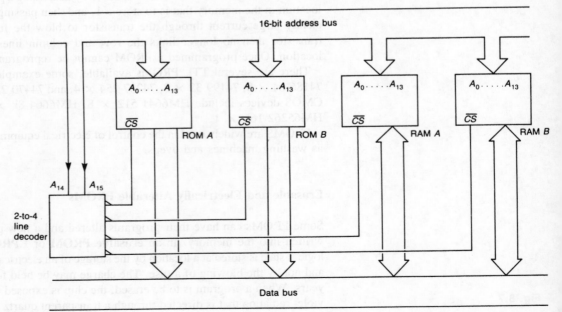

Fig. 8.6 Address decoding

address locations in the memories. Bits A_{14} and A_{15} are applied to a 2-to-4 line decoder whose four outputs are each applied to the $\overline{CS}$ pin of a memory. Only one of the $\overline{CS}$ pins is taken low by the decoder at any time and only that memory is then connected to the data bus and able to be read, or for a RAM be written to. The outputs of the non-selected memories are in a high impedance state.

Implementing a Combinational Logic Function using a ROM

Whenever a combinational logic function that is to be implemented has a large number of input variables and/or outputs it will often prove to be more economic to employ either a ROM or a *programmable logic array* (PLA).

A ROM can be made to implement a logic function by using it to store the truth table of that function. The function should be written in the sum-of-product form in which each term includes all of the input variables. Each input variable will be applied to an address line of the ROM. Then each combination of the input variables will address a particular memory location and thereby produce the required output signal.

Suppose that the function $F = \overline{A}\overline{B}C + A\overline{B}C + AB\overline{C}$ is to be implemented. There are three input variables, so a ROM with three address pins is required together with a 3-to-8 line decoder. The required ROM is shown by Fig. 8.7.

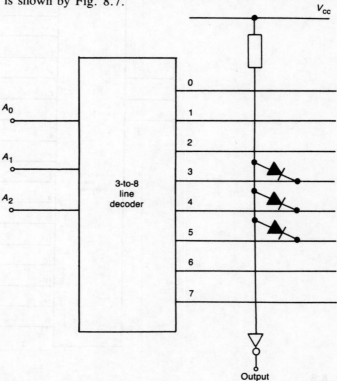

Fig. 8.7

When any of the lines 3, 4 or 5 is selected by an input address, that line is taken low and the associated diode conducts. The output line then goes low also. Since the outputs are all inverted an active output is indicated by the logical 1 state.

EXAMPLE 8.3

The equations

$$F_0 = A\bar{B}\bar{C}D + AB\bar{C}\bar{D} + A\bar{B}C\bar{D} + ABC\bar{D} + A\bar{B}CD + \bar{A}BCD + \bar{A}\bar{B}CD + \bar{A}BCD$$

$$F_1 = \bar{A}\bar{B}\bar{C}D + A\bar{B}C\bar{D} + \bar{A}BC\bar{D} + ABC\bar{D} + AB\bar{C}D + \bar{A}\bar{B}CD + ABCD$$

and

$$F_2 = \bar{A}\bar{B}C\bar{D} + A\bar{B}C\bar{D} + \bar{A}BC\bar{D} + ABC\bar{D} + A\bar{B}CD + \bar{A}BCD + ABCD$$

are to be implemented using a ROM. Obtain the desired circuit.

Solution
The required ROM is shown by Fig. 8.8.

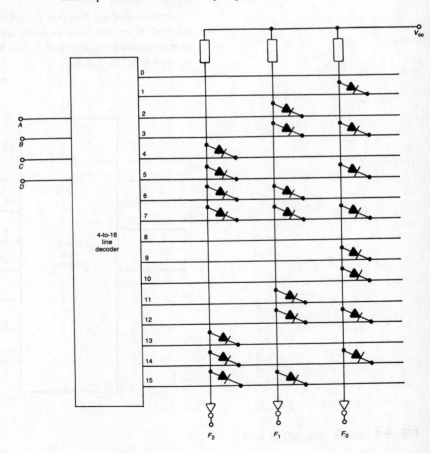

Fig. 8.8

Programmable Logic Devices

Large-scale integrated *programmable logic devices* (PLDs) variously known as **gate arrays**, or **programmable logic arrays** (PLA), or **programmable array logic** (PAL) are circuits which can be programmed to perform a specific combinational and/or sequential logical function. The circuit consists essentially of an array of gates formed into two matrices and, perhaps, flip-flops and more complex circuits. Almost any random logic design can be realized at a lower cost than would be possible using SSI/MSI integrated circuits. One PLD can perform the function of several SSI/MSI devices.

The design of a circuit that is to perform a required complex logical operation can be carried out using traditional methods such as Boolean algebra and the Karnaugh map. Once a design has been finalized, its implementation can be achieved in one of two ways: either the required design is sent, using custom-designer forms, to the chip manufacturer for implementation; or the design can be implemented by the designer. PLDs of the first type are often known as **mask-programmable** devices. A gate array is manufactured in a standard unprogrammed form and is later (on receipt of a particular circuit design) 'wired' to give the wanted circuit by the application of a metallization conductive pattern. All gate arrays are standard devices until they have been programmed to perform some particular circuit function.

Other PLD chips, often known as **field-programmable**, can be programmed by the user. Mask- and field-programmable arrays are, in this sense, analogous to the ROM and to the PROM that were discussed earlier. Field-programmable devices are well suited to small-scale production. For large volume production of a circuit it is generally more economic to employ mask-programmable devices.

The basic block diagram of a PLD is shown in Fig. 8.9. The input digital codeword is applied to the input buffer and the complement of each literal is generated. The AND matrix is able to handle any one of 2^{n+1} input combinations and each of these can be programmed to produce a required result. In a PLA the OR matrix is programmed to produce particular combinations of the words held in the AND matrix and these are passed, via the output buffers, to the output terminals. A PAL also has a programmable AND matrix but the OR matrix is fixed and not programmable. The dimensions of a PLD are $m \times n \times p$, where m is the number of inputs, n is the number of product terms, and p is the number of outputs.

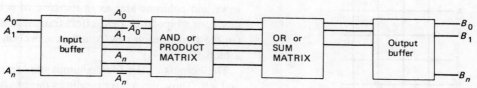

Fig. 8.9 Block diagram of a PLD

The PLD differs from the ROM in that, whereas the ROM employs an address decoder, the PLD employs a *programmable address matrix* (the AND matrix). The size of the address decoder in a ROM *doubles* for each additional address bit: a 256 × 8 ROM will require 8 address bits and a 512 × 8 ROM will require 9 address bits. In each case the address decoder must be able to access all of the locations in the ROM *even though they may not all be used*. This means that the use of an address decoder is inherently inefficient.

Since a PLD employs a programmable address matrix instead of an address decoder, it is able to select any one of a number of input states. Because of this, a PLD does not need to store, and be able to access, unused minterms.

The address matrix does not have a fixed size in relation to the number of its inputs. For example, a 16-input PROM would require an address decoder able to decode 2^{16} words; a PLD with the same number of inputs need only be large enough to store (say) 48 words or product terms. This means that *any* 48 out of 2^{16} or 65 536 words are used. A PLD permits the programming of simplified Boolean equations, whereas the canonical form of an expression is necessary for a ROM. A consequence of this is that a PLD can have more inputs than a ROM.

Programmable logic devices are available from various manufacturers in the TTL, CMOS and ECL logic families. One manufacturer, for example, offers: TTL arrays with 250, 550, 1000 or 2000 gates; CMOS arrays with 400, 800, 1300, 2100, 4100, 6500 or 11 000 gates; and ECL arrays with 300, 1200 or 2000 gates. The most common form of CMOS PLD is the *Generic Array Logic* (GAL) device.

A circuit which would ordinarily require several SSI/MSI devices can be produced as a single-chip gate array. This will give a significant reduction in the physical space occupied by the circuit, and in costs, and, because of a considerable reduction in the number of soldered connections, an increase in reliability. Unfortunately, the cost of developing a custom-built LSI chip is very high and often cannot be justified. This is the very point at which the use of a PLD, either mask or field programmed, would be considered since it allows an LSI solution to a problem at not too great a cost.

The Principle of a Programmable Logic Array

Figure 8.10 shows a simple matrix. The required connections between rows and columns are, as in the case of a ROM, established by a diode, or a bipolar or field-effect transistor appropriately connected. (In the figure, each row/column connection is indicated merely by a blob.)

The outputs of the four columns are, respectively, AB, $\bar{A}B$, $A\bar{B}$, and $\bar{A}\bar{B}$. Thus, the matrix produces the *product* of each combination of the inputs. The matrix is therefore known as the product or AND matrix. It should be noted that a product term need not include all

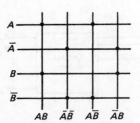

Fig. 8.10 Simple matrix

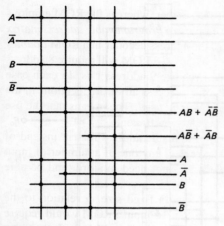

Fig. 8.11 Basic PLA

of the inputs; any number of the inputs can always be treated as 'don't cares'.

If the outputs of the AND matrix are used as the inputs to a second matrix, as shown by Fig. 8.11, a simple PLA will be produced. The top output of this second matrix is equal to $AB + \bar{A}\bar{B}$, the next output is equal to $A\bar{B} + \bar{A}B$, and so on. Each of the outputs is the *sum* of the AND matrix outputs to which it is connected. For this reason the second matrix is known as the sum or OR matrix.

EXAMPLE 8.4

Design a simple PLA to implement the Boolean equations

$$F_0 = ABCD + \bar{A}B\bar{C}D + A\bar{B}C\bar{D} + \bar{A}B\bar{C}\bar{D} \text{ and}$$
$$F_1 = AB\bar{C}\bar{D} + \bar{A}\bar{B}CD$$

Solution
The AND matrix must generate each of the wanted product terms and then these will be summed by the OR matrix to produce the required outputs F_0 and F_1.

Figure 8.12 shows the required circuit.

An alternative method of representing the AND and OR matrices is commonly employed. All of the product terms generated by the AND matrix can be shown as being generated by AND gates. Similarly, each sum-of-product term, generated by the OR matrix, can be shown as appearing at the output of an OR gate. Using this alternative method of representation, the solution to Exercise 8.4 can be redrawn and this has been done in Fig. 8.13.

EXAMPLE 8.5

Implement, using a PLA, the Boolean equation

$$F = AB + \bar{B}\bar{C} + BC$$

Solution
See Figs 8.14a and b, respectively.

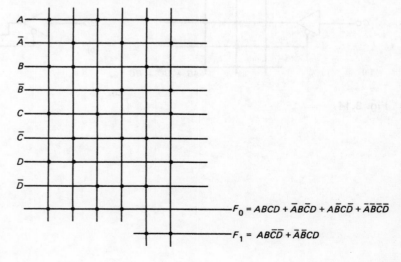

Fig. 8.12

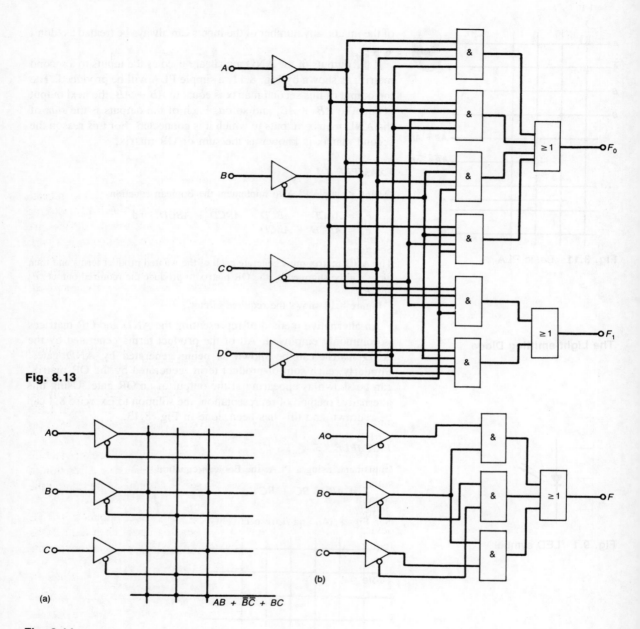

Fig. 8.13

Fig. 8.14

9 Visual Displays

Visual displays are often employed in electronic equipment to indicate the numerical value of some quantity, e.g. digital watches, electronic calculators, and digital voltmeters. A variety of display devices are available but in this book the discussion will be limited to just two; namely, the light-emitting diode or LED, and the liquid crystal display or LCD. The circuitry needed to drive the display can be constructed using SSI gates but MSI decoder/driver ICs are commonly employed, sometimes in the same package as the LEDs.

The Light-emitting Diode

The majority of **light-emitting diodes** or **LEDs** are either gallium phosphide (GaP) or gallium-arsenide-phosphide (GaAsP) devices. An LED radiates energy in the visible part of the electromagnetic spectrum when the forward bias voltage applied across the diode exceeds the voltage that turns it ON. This voltage depends upon the type of LED and the colour of the light it emits (see Table 9.1). The symbol for a LED is shown by Fig. 9.1.

The current flowing in a LED must not be allowed to exceed a safe figure, generally some 20–60 mA, and if necessary a resistor of suitable value must be connected in series with the diode to limit the current.

Often a LED is connected between one of the outputs of a TTL device and either earth or +5 V depending upon when the LED is required to glow visibly. If, for example, a LED is expected to glow

Fig. 9.1 LED symbol

Table 9.1 LED types

Colour	Material	Wavelength (peak radiation) (nm)	Forward voltage at 10 mA current (V)
Red	GaAsP	650	1.6
Green	GaP	565	2.1
Yellow	GaAsP	590	2.0
Orange	GaAsP	625	1.8
Blue	SiC	480	3.0

Blue LEDs are a fairly recent development and these devices use silicon carbide (SiC).

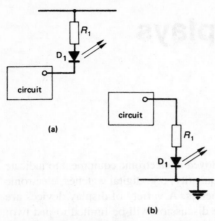

(a)

(b)

Fig. 9.2 Use of LEDs as indicators

Liquid Crystal Displays

when the output to which it is connected is *low*, the device should be connected as shown in Fig. 9.2*a*. Suppose the low voltage to be 0.4 V and the sink current to be 16 mA. Then if the LED voltage drop is 1.6 V the value of the series resistor will be

$$(5 - 1.6 - 0.4)/(16 \times 10^{-3}) = 188 \text{ ohms}$$

When the output of the device is high ($\simeq 5$ V), no current flows and the LED remains dark. When the LED is to glow to indicate the high output condition, the circuit shown in Fig. 9.2*b* must be used. Now

$$R_1 = (5 - 1.6)/(16 \times 10^{-3}) = 213 \text{ ohms}$$

When a LED is reverse biased it acts very much like a zener diode with a low breakdown voltage ($\simeq 4$ V).

Light-emitting diodes are commonly used because they are cheap, reliable, easy to interface, and are readily available from a number of sources. Their main disadvantage is that their luminous efficiency is low, typically 1.5 lumens/watt.

A solid crystal is a material in which the molecules are arranged in a rigid lattice structure. If the temperature of the material is increased above its melting point, the liquid that is formed will tend to retain much of the orderly molecular structure. The material is then said to be in its *liquid crystalline phase*. There are two classes of liquid crystal known, respectively, as *nematic* and *smetic* but only the former is used for display devices.

A nematic liquid crystal does not radiate light but, instead, it interferes with the passage of light whenever it is under the influence of an applied electric field. There are two ways in which the optical properties of a liquid crystal can be influenced by an electric field. These are called *dynamic scattering* and *twisted nematic*. The former was commonly employed in the past but now its application is mainly restricted to large-sized displays. The commonly met liquid crystal displays, e.g. those in digital watches and hand calculators, are all of the twisted nematic type.

The construction of a **liquid crystal** cell is shown in Fig. 9.3*a*. A layer of a liquid crystal material is placed in between two glass plates that have transparent metal film electrodes deposited on to their interior faces. A reflective surface, or mirror, is situated on the outer side of the lower glass plate (it may be deposited on its surface). The conductive material is generally either tin oxide or a tin oxide/indium oxide mixture and it will transmit light with about 90% efficiency. The incident light upon the upper glass plate is polarized in such a way that, if there is *zero* electric field between the plates, the light is able to pass right through and arrive at the reflective surface. Here it is reflected back and the reflected light travels through the cell and emerges from the upper plate (Fig. 9.3*b*). If a voltage is applied across the plates (Fig. 9.3*c*) the polarization of the light entering the cell

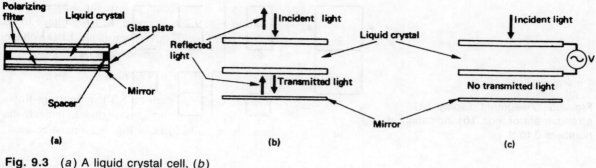

Fig. 9.3 (a) A liquid crystal cell, (b) and (c) operation of a liquid crystal cell

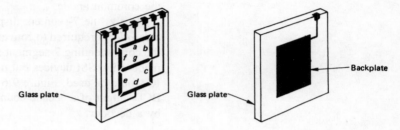

Fig. 9.4 LCD 7-segment display

is altered and it is then no longer able to propagate as far as the reflective surface. Thus no light returns from the upper surface of the cell and the display appears to be *dark*. Because the LCD does not emit light, it dissipates little power.

Liquid crystal displays, unlike LEDs, are not available as single units and are generally manufactured in the form of a 7-segment display. The metal oxide film electrode on the surface of the upper glass plate is formed into the shape of the required 7 segments, each of which is taken to a separate contact, and the lower glass plate has a common electrode or *backplate* deposited on it. The idea is shown by Fig. 9.4. With this arrangement a voltage can be applied between the backplate and any one, or more, of the seven segments to make that, or those, particular segment(s) appear to be dark and thereby display the required number.

Nematic liquid crystal displays possess a number of advantages which have led to their widespread use in battery-operated equipment. First, their power consumption is very small, about 1 μW per segment (much less than the LED); second, their visibility is not affected by bright incident light (such as sunlight); and, third, they are compatible with low-power NMOS/CMOS circuitry.

Seven-segment, 16-segment and Dot Matrix Displays

Seven-segment displays are generally used as numerical indicators and consist of a number of LEDs arranged in seven segments as shown in Fig. 9.5a. Any number between 0 and 9 can be indicated by lighting the appropriate segments. This is shown by Fig. 9.5b. A typical 7-segment display is manufactured in a 14-pin dil package with the

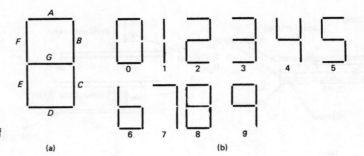

Fig. 9.5 7-segment display: (a) arrangement of leds, (b) indication of numbers 0 to 9

cathode of each LED being brought out to a terminal together with the common anode.

Clearly, the 7-segment display needs a 7-bit input signal and so a *decoder* is required to convert the digital signal to be displayed into the corresponding 7-segment signal. Decoder/driver circuits *can* be made using SSI devices but more usually a ROM or a custom-built IC would be used. Figure 9.6 shows one arrangement, in which the BCD output of a decade counter is converted to a 7-segment signal by a decoder.

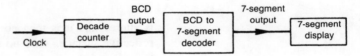

Fig. 9.6 BCD decade counter with 7-segment display

When a count in excess of 9 is required, a second counter must be used and be connected in the manner shown by Fig. 9.7. The tens counter is connected to the output of the final flip-flop of the units counter in the same way as the flip-flops inside the counters are connected.

The design of a 7-segment display starts with the truth table for the circuit. This is given by Table 9.2; note that numbers greater than 9 do not appear in the display and so they are 'don't cares'.

From the truth table a number of segment maps can be obtained, each of which maps the inputs which must be high for a segment to be illuminated.

Thus segment *a* is ON when the input decimal number is 0, 2, 3, 5, 7, 8 or 9. Hence

$$a = \overline{A}\,\overline{B}\,\overline{C}\,\overline{D} + \overline{A}B\overline{C}\,\overline{D} + \overline{A}B\overline{C}D + A\overline{B}\,\overline{C}\,\overline{D} + AB\overline{C}\,\overline{D} + \overline{A}\,\overline{B}C\overline{D} + A\overline{B}\,\overline{C}D$$

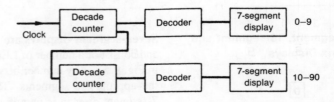

Fig. 9.7 Decade counters arranged to give a count in excess of 9

Table 9.2

Decimal number displayed	Inputs				Outputs						
	D	C	B	A	a	b	c	d	e	f	g
0	0	0	0	0	1	1	1	1	1	1	0
1	0	0	0	1	0	1	1	0	0	0	0
2	0	0	1	0	1	1	0	1	1	0	1
3	0	0	1	1	1	1	1	1	0	0	1
4	0	1	0	0	0	1	1	0	0	1	1
5	0	1	0	1	1	0	1	1	0	1	1
6	0	1	1	0	0	0	1	1	1	1	1
7	0	1	1	1	1	1	1	0	0	0	0
8	1	0	0	0	1	1	1	1	1	1	1
9	1	0	0	1	1	1	1	0	0	1	1

Mapping

	A	A	$\bar{A}$	$\bar{A}$	
C	X	X	X	X	D
C	1	1	0	0	$\bar{D}$
$\bar{C}$	1	0	1	1	$\bar{D}$
$\bar{C}$	X	1	1	X	D
	B	$\bar{B}$	$\bar{B}$	B	

a

From the map

$$a = \bar{A}\bar{C} + AB + AC + D$$

Similarly for the other segments:

	A	A	$\bar{A}$	$\bar{A}$	
C	X	X	X	X	D
C	1	0	1	0	$\bar{D}$
$\bar{C}$	1	1	1	1	$\bar{D}$
$\bar{C}$	X	1	1	X	D
	B	$\bar{B}$	$\bar{B}$	B	

b

	A	A	$\bar{A}$	$\bar{A}$	
C	X	X	X	X	D
C	1	1	1	1	$\bar{D}$
$\bar{C}$	1	1	1	0	$\bar{D}$
$\bar{C}$	X	1	1	X	D
	B	$\bar{B}$	$\bar{B}$	B	

c

	A	A	$\bar{A}$	$\bar{A}$	
C	X	X	X	X	D
C	0	1	0	1	$\bar{D}$
$\bar{C}$	1	0	1	1	$\bar{D}$
$\bar{C}$	X	0	1	X	D
	B	$\bar{B}$	$\bar{B}$	B	

d

Map e:

	A		$\bar{A}$		
C	X	X	X	X	D
	0	0	0	1	$\bar{D}$
	0	0	1	1	D
$\bar{C}$	X	0	1	X	
	B	$\bar{B}$	B		

$\boxed{e}$

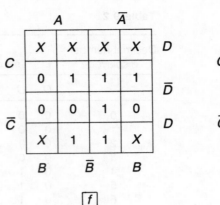

$\boxed{f}$

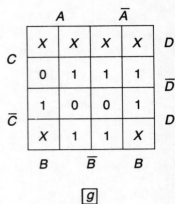

$\boxed{g}$

From the maps,

$$b = AB + \bar{A}\bar{B} + \bar{C} \qquad\qquad c = A + \bar{B} + C$$
$$d = \bar{A}B + \bar{A}C + B\bar{C} + A\bar{B}C \qquad e = \bar{A}\bar{B} + \bar{A}C$$
$$f = \bar{A}\bar{B} + \bar{B}C + \bar{A}C + D \qquad g = \bar{A}B + \bar{B}C + B\bar{C} + D$$

This logic can be implemented in one of the various ways described earlier. The ROM circuit is obtained by noting from Table 9.2 that (i) when 0 is to be displayed all segments except segment g are lit, (ii) when 1 is to be displayed only segments b and c are lit, and so on. The input lines 0 through 9 are normally held high and their associated diodes are non-conducting. The vertical lines are held high also. It can be seen that for a segment to light, the LED must be forward biased and for this the segment line must be low. Hence none of the segments are lit. If, say, input line 1 is selected that line is taken low and this causes the two associated diodes to conduct to take their connected output lines low also. When an output line is low the segment LED connected to it is forward biased and lights and hence by taking the appropriate segment lines low the required number is displayed.

A commonly employed MSI circuit is the TTL 7447 BCD-to-7-segment decoder/driver. This IC has four input pins, A, B, C and D to which the BCD input signal is applied and seven output pins, labelled as a through to g. When an output is high the segment to which it is connected lights. If, for example, the input signal is 0101, outputs a, f, g, c and d go high so that the decimal number 5 is illuminated.

The IC includes a facility known as *remote blanking*. Two other pins, labelled as RB_{in} and RB_{out} are provided. If the RB_{in} pin of the most significant 7-segment display is earthed *and* inputs A, B, C and D are all low, then its RB_{out} pin will be low and so are all segment outputs. The RB_{out} pin of each display is connected to the RB_{in} pin of the next most significant 7-segment display. This connection ensures that leading 0s in a displayed decimal number are not visible, e.g. for a 4-bit display 617 would be displayed and not 0617.

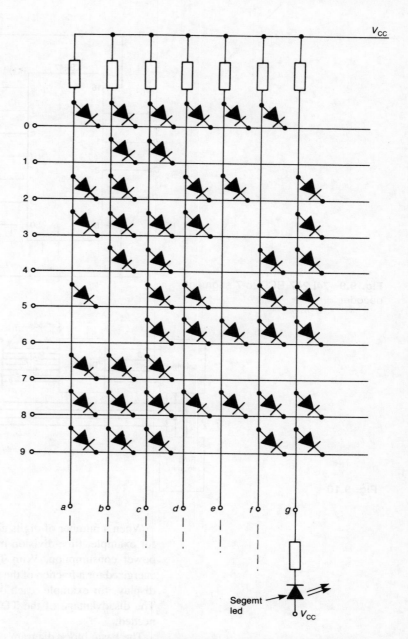

Fig. 9.8   ROM BCD-to-7 segment decoder

Other BCD-to-7-segment decoders are available in the TTL logic family, such as the 7446/8/9 and the 74246/7/8/9, while the CMOS family includes the 4511. Fig. 9.9 shows how the 74LS247 circuit is connected. The 247 has active-low outputs and so it can directly drive a LED display. It may be necessary to limit the current that flows through an ON LED and this is the function of the series resistors. Pins 4 and 5 are outputs which if connected to the display can be used for blanking purposes.

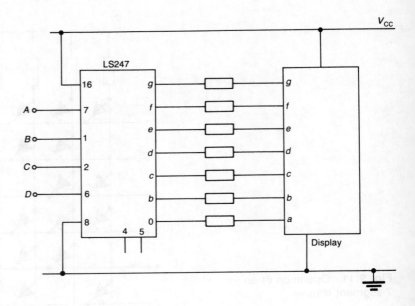

Fig. 9.9 74L247 BCD-to-7 segment decoder

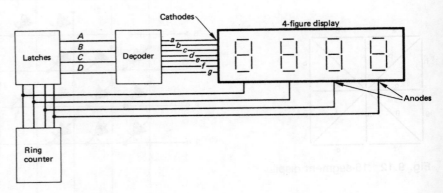

Fig. 9.10

When a number of digits are to be displayed, as in a digital meter for example, time-division multiplexing is often used to reduce the power consumption. With TDM each digit of the display is only energized for a fraction of the time the number is displayed. In a 6-digit display, for example, each digit is energized for 1/6th of the time. The disadvantage of the TDM system is the extra circuitry that is needed.

The basic block diagram of such an arrangement is given in Fig. 9.10. When an output of the ring counter goes high the data held in the latches are enabled and are passed on to the decoder and, at the same time, the appropriate LED display is also enabled. It may also be necessary to latch the inputs to the decoder so that a clear and steady display is obtained. Otherwise, the display may change so rapidly that the numbers cannot be recognized.

The voltages applied to a LCD must be alternating with zero dc component to prevent any electrolytic plating action taking place that

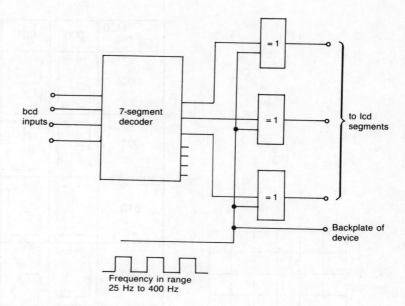

Fig. 9.11 Operation of an lcd
7-segment display

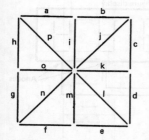

Fig. 9.12 16-segment display

would damage the device. The basic arrangement used is shown in Fig. 9.11, suitable LCD decoder/drivers are provided in the CMOS family, e.g. the 4055 and the 4056.

Integrated circuits are also available that incorporate photoelectric or LCD devices. Examples are the Texas TIL 306/7. These devices include a BCD counter, a 4-bit latch, and a 7-segment decoder and LED driver, all in a 16-pin package. The circuits can be used in applications where the clock pulse count is to be displayed, the choice of circuit being determined by a requirement for a decimal point to appear either side of the displayed number. Several devices can be connected together so that larger numbers can be displayed.

Similar ICs are also available for the display of BCD, 4-bit binary, or hexadecimal data.

If alphanumeric characters are to be displayed either a 16-segment, or a dot-matrix, display is necessary.

A 16-segment display uses 16 LEDs or LCDs arranged in the manner shown by Fig. 9.12. Applying voltages to the display to illuminate the appropriate segments will cause the characters shown in Fig. 9.13 to become visible. A number of 16-segment display driver modules are available, one example being the NSM 1416.

With a dot matrix display each alphanumeric character is indicated by illuminating a number of dots in a 5 × 7 dot matrix. To allow for lower-case letters and for spaces in between adjacent rows and columns each character fount is allocated a 6 × 12 space. Figure 9.14a shows a 6 × 12 dot matrix. Every location in the dot matrix has an LED connected, as shown by Fig. 9.14b, for the top two rows of the matrix only. All the cathodes of the LEDs in one row, and all of the anodes in one column are connected together. By addressing

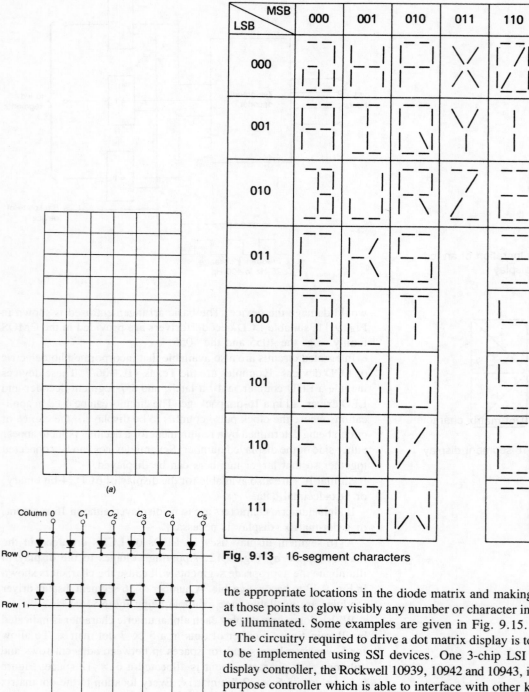

Fig. 9.13 16-segment characters

Fig. 9.14 6 × 12 dot matrix

the appropriate locations in the diode matrix and making the LEDs at those points to glow visibly any number or character in the set can be illuminated. Some examples are given in Fig. 9.15.

The circuitry required to drive a dot matrix display is too complex to be implemented using SSI devices. One 3-chip LSI dot matrix display controller, the Rockwell 10939, 10942 and 10943, is a general-purpose controller which is able to interface with other kinds of dot matrix as well as a LED type. The controller can drive up to 46 dots and up to 20 characters selected out of the full 96 character ASCII code.

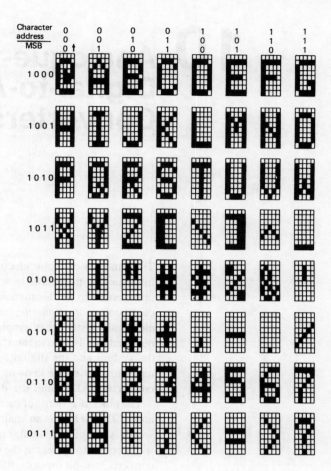

Fig. 9.15 Dot matrix characters

10 Analogue-to-Digital and Digital-to-Analogue Converters

The function of many electronic systems is to receive some input information, process it in some way, and then pass the processed information to its destination. Nearly always, the information is of continuous, or *analogue*, nature but, increasingly nowadays, the electronic system may employ digital techniques. Circuitry is then required that is able to interface between the analogue world outside the system and the digital system itself. Two interface circuits are necessary which are known, respectively, as the **analogue-to-digital converter** (ADC) and the **digital-to-analogue converter** (DAC).

The block diagrams for each of these devices are given in Figs 10.1*a* and *b*. The ADC has an analogue signal applied to its input terminals which is sampled at regular intervals, and an equivalent digital signal is generated to appear at the output terminals. Conversely, the DAC converts an *n*-bit input digital signal into the corresponding analogue signal.

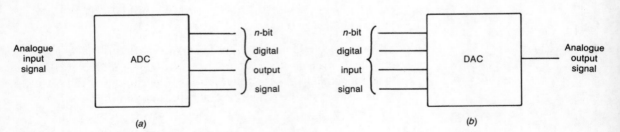

Fig. 10.1 Block diagram of (*a*) an analogue-to-digital converter, (*b*) a digital-to-analogue converter

Digital-to-Analogue Converters

The circuit of one form of DAC is shown in Fig. 10.2. An operational amplifier (op-amp) is connected as a summing amplifier with a number of inputs equal to the number of bits per input digital word. The resistor R connected to the MSB input D_3 has twice the resistance of the op-amp feedback resistor R_f. The next MSB resistor has

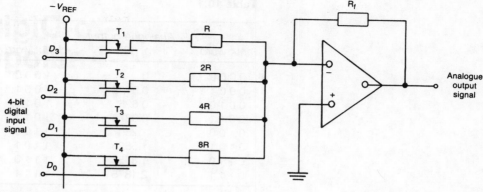

Fig. 10.2 A weighted resistor DAC

twice the resistance again, i.e. $2R$, and so on for each of the remaining input resistors. If there are n inputs the LSB resistor should have a resistance of $2nR$ Ω; in the figure $R_f = 1$ kΩ and $n = 4$ so that the LSB resistance is of resistance value $2^4 = 16$ kΩ.

When a digital signal is applied to the input terminals of the DAC each input bit that is at the logic 1 voltage level will cause a current to flow in the associated resistor. If an input bit is at the logic 0 level zero current will flow in that input. The op-amp sums the currents flowing and this total current flows in the feedback resistor R_f to develop an output voltage. The magnitude of this output voltage is proportional to the total current flowing and hence to the digital input word.

If, for example, the digital input word is 1001, $R_f = 5000$ Ω and the logic 1 voltage level is $+5$ V, current will flow in the inputs D_0 and D_3 whose magnitudes are:

$$I_3 = 5/(10 \times 10^3) = 0.5 \text{ mA}$$
$$I_0 = 5/(16 \times 5 \times 10^3) = 5/(80 \times 10^3) = 0.0625 \text{ mA}$$
$$I_1 = I_2 = 0$$

The total current flowing to the op-amp is 0.5625 mA and so the output voltage is equal to $0.5625 \times 10^{-3} \times 5000 = 2.8125$ V. If, now, the input digital word changes to 1101 the currents I_3 and I_0 will be unchanged but there will now also be a current I_2.

$$I_2 = 5/(20 \times 10^3) = 0.25 \text{ mA}.$$

The total current is now 0.8125 mA and the output voltage is 4.0625 V. Table 10.1 gives the output voltage produced by each of the possible input digital words. These values are shown plotted in Fig. 10.3 and illustrate that a stepped analogue output voltage signal is obtained. The magnitude of each step could be halved, and resolution improved, if an 8-bit input signal were to be employed.

Although the basic concept is fairly simple its practical implementation is not. The requirement for the input resistors to be *binary weighted* is difficult, and hence expensive, to satisfy. For this reason the weighted-resistor DAC is only employed where a low resolution

Table 10.1

Input word	Analogue output (V)	Input word	Analogue output (V)
0 0 0 0	0	1 0 0 0	2.5
0 0 0 1	0.3125	1 0 0 1	2.8125
0 0 1 0	0.625	1 0 1 0	3.125
0 0 1 1	0.9375	1 0 1 1	3.4375
0 1 0 0	1.25	1 1 0 0	3.75
0 1 0 1	1.5625	1 1 0 1	4.0625
0 1 1 0	1.875	1 1 1 0	4.375
0 1 1 1	2.1875	1 1 1 1	4.6875

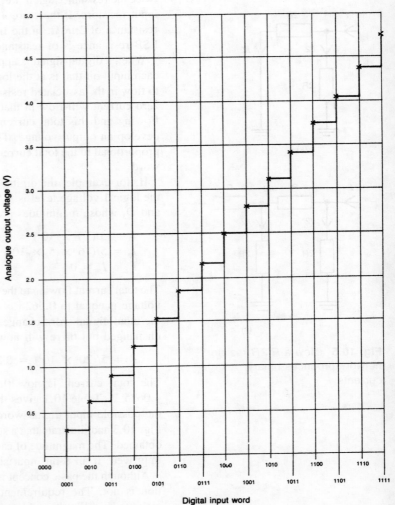

Fig. 10.3 Output voltage of a DAC

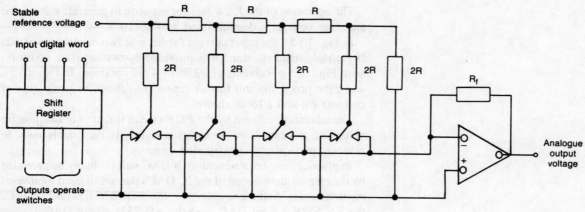

Fig. 10.4   *R/2R* DAC

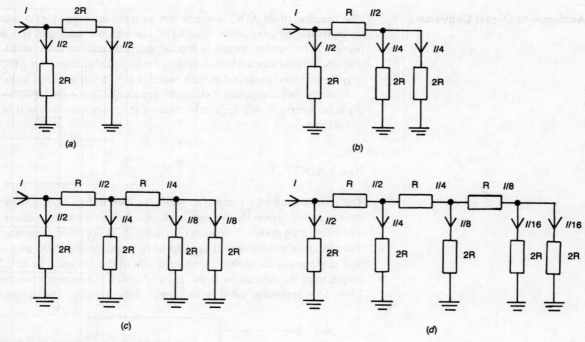

Fig. 10.5   How a *R/2R* resistor
network produces binary weighted
currents

is wanted so that a 4-bit input is adequate. It is not practicable to
produce an IC version of this type of DAC.

A commonly employed DAC is the *R/2R* circuit given in Fig. 10.4.
The circuit uses resistors of only two different values, one of which
is twice the other. The wanted analogue voltage is obtained by switching resistors either to earth or to the op-amp. The total current that
is switched is passed through the feedback resistor of the op-amp to
generate the output voltage. The switching of the resistors is controlled
by a shift register to which the input digital word is applied.

The operation of the $R/2R$ resistor network to generate the wanted analogue voltage is demonstrated by Fig. 10.5.

In Fig. 10.5a the input current I splits into two equal parts of $I/2$. If the right-hand resistor $2R$ is provided by two separate resistors, as in Fig. 10.5b, currents of $I/2$ and $I/4$ are obtained. In Figs 10.5c and d the process is still further repeated to allow the generation of currents $I/8$ and $I/16$ as shown.

The advantage offered by the $R/2R$ circuit is that only two precise values of resistance are necessary and this is reasonably easy to achieve, particularly in integrated circuitry.

In practice, any requirement for a DAC will probably be provided by the employment of one of the IC DACs that are offered by several manufacturers. Some examples are: the AD 7226 quad 8-bit DAC, the ZN 558E-8 8-bit DAC, and the AD 7521 12-bit DAC.

Analogue-to-Digital Converters

The function of an ADC is to convert an input analogue signal into an equivalent digital form. The ADC samples the analogue signal present at its input terminals at regular intervals and for each sample outputs a digital word which indicates the sampled voltage. An ADC may be arranged to output its data either in parallel or in serial form.

A number of competing techniques are available for analogue-to-digital conversion, but here only three of the more common will be considered.

Ramp ADC

The basic circuit of a ramp-type ADC is given in Fig. 10.6. At the start of a conversion the counter is cleared so that it has zero count. The clock then makes the counter go through its counting sequence. The output of the counter is applied to the input to the DAC and is also made available to the output terminals of the circuit. The DAC output then increments in steps, each of which corresponds to one LSB and is applied to the inverting input of the op-amp. The op-amp

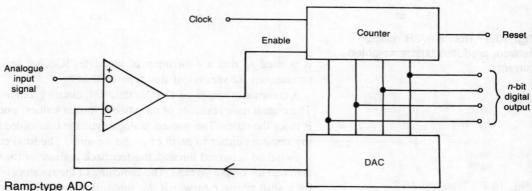

Fig. 10.6 Ramp-type ADC

is operated as a voltage comparator, hence when the DAC output voltage becomes more positive than the analogue input voltage the comparator switches and its output goes low and disables the counter. The count reached then indicates the voltage of the analogue signal.

The counter must then be reset to zero for a new count to begin and another conversion to commence. The circuit is only able to produce one conversion for every 2^n clock pulses and so it is only suitable for use in situations where the analogue signal changes only slowly.

Tracking ADC

A much improved performance can be obtained at very little extra cost if the counter in Fig. 10.6 is replaced by an up-down counter. The circuit of a tracking ADC is given in Fig. 10.7.

The voltage applied to the inverting input of the comparator-connected op-amp is the difference between the analogue signal voltage and the output voltage of the DAC. If this difference is positive the output of the comparator will be low and the counter will cause the DAC output to increment by one LSB. This happens repeatedly until the difference voltage becomes negative, i.e. the output voltage of the DAC is more positive than is the analogue input voltage. The comparator will then switch and its output will go high. This makes the counter commence down-counting. At all instants in time the comparator will switch the counter to count in the direction (up or down) which tends to reduce the difference voltage.

Once an initial lock has been established the ADC will *track* any changes in the analogue voltage so long as they are not too rapid. Any break in the signal will mean that the lock is lost. Continuously present at the counter output is the binary-coded equivalent of the analogue voltage. The purpose of the D flip-flop is to ensure that there is an adequate time period between any change in the comparator output and the next count.

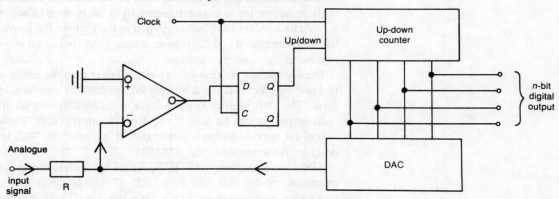

Fig. 10.7 Tracking ADC

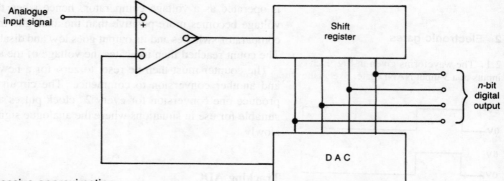

Fig. 10.8 Successive approximation ADC

Successive Approximation ADC

The block diagram of a successive approximation ADC is given in Fig. 10.8. The circuit operates by repeatedly comparing the analogue signal voltage with a number of approximate voltages which are generated at the DAC output.

Initially, the shift register is cleared and then the DAC output is zero. The first clock pulse applies the MSB of the register to the DAC. The output of the DAC is then one-half of its full scale voltage range (FSR). If the analogue voltage is greater than FSR/2 the MSB is retained (stored by a latch), if it is less than the FSR/2 the MSB is lost. The next clock pulse applies the next lower MSB to the DAC, producing a DAC output of FSR/4. If the MSB had been retained the total DAC output voltage is now 3FSR/4; if the MSB has been lost the output of the DAC is now FSR/4. In either case the analogue and DAC voltages are again compared. If the analogue voltage is the larger of the two the second MSB is retained (latched); if it is not the second MSB is lost.

A succession of similar trials are carried out and after each the shift register output bit is either retained by a latch or it is not. Once $n + 1$ clock pulses have been supplied to the register the conversion has been completed and the register output gives the digital word that represents the analogue voltage.

The conversion process is very much faster than for either of the two previous methods and it is easily implemented in integrated circuit form. The shift register needs a latch at each of its outputs so that each output bit can be held if required. Some registers, known as successive approximation registers (SAR), are available with latches on-chip. An example is the AM2505.

ADCs are manufactured in IC packages by several sources; some examples are the AD 670 8-bit, AD 575 10-bit, AD 574 12-bit successive approximation ADCs, and the ZN 433 10-bit tracking ADC.

Exercises

2 Electronic gates

2.1 The waveforms given in Fig. E.2.1 are applied to the inputs of a 3-input NAND gate. Sketch the output waveform.

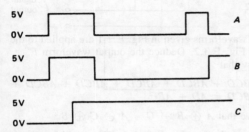

Fig. E.2.1

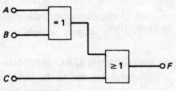

Fig. E.2.2

2.2 Obtain an expression for the output F of the circuit given in Fig. E.2.2.

2.3 The waveforms shown in Fig. E.2.1 are applied to the input terminals of the circuits of Fig. E.2.3. Draw the output waveforms.

2.4 Obtain an expression for the output F of the circuits of Fig. E.2.3.

2.5 Write down the truth tables for the circuits given in Fig. E.2.5.

2.6 Determine the expression for the output F of the circuit in Fig. E.2.6.

2.7 Redraw each circuit in Fig. E.2.3 using NAND and/or NOR gates.

2.8 In the circuit of Fig. E.2.6 the output is 0. Determine the logical states of each of the inputs.

2.9 Draw the British Standard symbol for a NOR gate and give its truth table if there are four inputs. Show how the same logical function could be obtained using relay contacts.

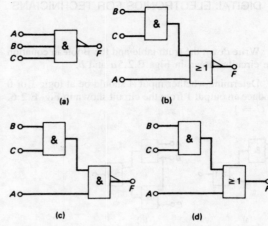

Fig. E.2.3

2.10 Connect the pins of the NAND gate IC given in Fig. 4.8 on p. 46 to produce an OR gate.

2.11 Draw a logic diagram to show how the functions (i) $F = AB + AC$, (ii) $F = A(B + C) + BC$ can be generated.

2.12 The waveforms shown in Fig. E.2.4 are applied to the input of

    (i) a three-input NAND gate, and
    (ii) a three-input NOR gate.

For each case determine the output waveform.

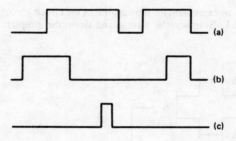

Fig. E.2.4

2.13 Write down the truth table for (i) a three-input NAND gate, (ii) a three-input NOR gate, and (iii) a NOT gate. Also give the corresponding Boolean expressions.

2.14 Draw circuits to perform the logical operations

    (i) $F = A \cdot B \cdot C + D \cdot E$
    (ii) $F = (A + B + C) \cdot (D + E)$

2.15 Write down the truth table and the Boolean equation of the circuits shown in Figs E.2.5a and b.

2.16 Determine whether input A should be at logic 1 or 0 to produce an output 1 from the circuit shown in Fig. E.2.6. B = C = 1.

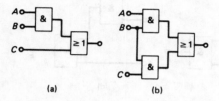

(a)   (b)

Fig. E.2.5

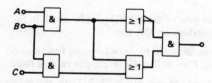

Fig. E.2.6

3 Simplification of Boolean Equations

3.1 For the circuit shown in Fig. E.2.6 obtain a Boolean expression for the output X of the circuit. Simplify the equation if possible and then draw the simplified circuit.

3.2 Obtain an expression for the output F of the circuit given in Fig. E.3.1. Simplify the circuit and draw the simpler alternative.

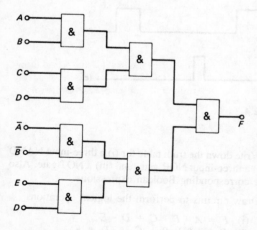

Fig. E.3.1

3.3 Derive an expression for the output of the circuit given in Fig. E.3.2.

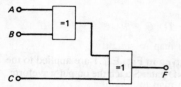

Fig. E.3.2

3.4 The waveforms given in Fig. E.2.1 are applied to the circuit of Fig. E.3.2. Deduce the output waveform F.
Show that

$$\bar{A}BC\bar{D} + \bar{A}BCD + A\bar{B}CD + A\bar{B}CD + AB\bar{C}D +$$
$$ABCD = AD + \bar{A}BC$$

3.5 Prove that $A \oplus B \oplus C = A \oplus C \oplus B$.

3.6 Express the function $F = A + BC$ in product-of-sum form.

3.7 Use a truth table to prove that

$$A + \bar{A}B = A + B$$

3.8 Use a truth table to prove that

$$A(\bar{A} + B) = AB$$

3.9 Evaluate $F = (A + B)(B + C)$ when

(a) $A = B = C = 0$
(b) $A = B = C = 1$
(c) $A = 1, B = C = 0$.

3.10 Show that

(a) $\overline{\bar{A}B} = A + \bar{A}B$

(b) $\overline{A\bar{B} + \bar{A}B} = AB + \bar{A}\bar{B}$

(c) $A(A + B) = A$

3.11 Simplify

(a) $F = \overline{A + B + \bar{A} + B}$

(b) $F = \overline{A\bar{B} + \bar{A} + B}$

(c) $F = (AB + \bar{C})(A + BC)$

(d) $F = \overline{(AC + D)(\bar{A}C + B)}$

3.12 Show that $(AB + \bar{C}) + (\bar{A} + \bar{B})C = 1$.

3.13 Show that

$$B(AD + BC)(\bar{A} + \bar{D})\bar{C}(\bar{A} + \bar{D}) = 0.$$

3.14 Express $F = AB\bar{C} + A\bar{B}C + \bar{A}\bar{B}C$ in product-of-sums form.

3.15 Express $F = (A + B + \bar{C})(A + \bar{B} + C)(\bar{A} + \bar{B} + \bar{C})$ in sum-of-products form.

3.16 Show that

$$(B + D)(D + C)(A + D) = D + ABC$$

3.17 Show that

$$(B + D)(A + D)(C + B)(C + A) = AB + CD$$

3.18 Use a Karnaugh map to simplify

$$F = A\bar{B}C + \bar{A}\bar{B}C + \bar{A}B\bar{C} + A\bar{B}\bar{C} + ABC$$

3.19 Use a Karnaugh map to simplify

$$F = AB\bar{C} + ABC + \bar{A}B\bar{C} + \bar{A}\bar{B}\bar{C}$$

Then loop the squares marked with 0 to obtain the minimal solution for $\bar{F}$. Invert $\bar{F}$ to check with the answer obtained in the first part of the question.

3.20 Use a Karnaugh map to minimize the equation

$$F = \bar{A}BC\bar{D} + \bar{A}B\bar{C}D + A\bar{B}CD + AB\bar{C}\bar{D} + ABCD + \bar{A}BCD$$

3.21 Use a Karnaugh map to minimize

$$F = (AB + \bar{B}\bar{C})(\bar{A}C + \overline{ABD} + BCD)$$

3.22 Use a Karnaugh map to minimize

$$F = A\bar{B} + \bar{C}D + C + \bar{B}CD$$

3.23 Use a Karnaugh map to minimize

$$F = \bar{A}\bar{B}C\bar{D} + \bar{A}\bar{B}\bar{C}D + AB\bar{C}D + \bar{A}BCD + ABD + \bar{B}C\bar{D} + \bar{A}BC\bar{D}$$

3.24 Map the function

$$F = ABC + \bar{A}BCD + \bar{A}B\bar{C}D + ACD$$

Obtain the minimal solution for $\bar{F}$ by looping the 0 squares.

3.25 Map the function $F = AC + C\bar{D} + \bar{A}D + CD$ and then simplify (*a*) by looping 1s and (*b*) by looping 0s.

3.26 Simplify (*a*) algebraically and (*b*) by mapping the function

$$F = (A + B)B(C + D) + (EB + AC)DB$$

3.27 Minimize $F = (\overline{\bar{A}B + AB})(\bar{A} + \bar{B})(A + B)$

3.28 Minimize $F = \overline{AB(B + C)} + \overline{AB}(1 + C)$

3.29 Implement, using NAND gates only, the function $F = \overline{A + BC}$.

3.30 For your circuit in answer to **3.29** replace each NAND gate by a NOR gate and then determine the logical expression describing the new circuit.

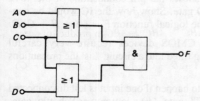

Fig. E.3.3

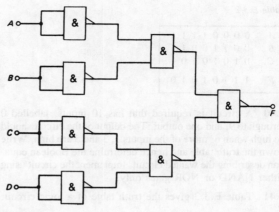

Fig. E.3.4

3.31 Implement the circuit given in Fig. E.3.3 using NOR gates only.

3.32 For the circuit of Fig. E.3.4 replace each NAND gate by a NOR gate and then determine the logical function performed by the new circuit.

3.33 Implement the function $F = A + BC(A + C)$ using NAND gates only.

3.34 Implement the function $F = \bar{A}B + BC + \bar{D}$ using (*a*) NAND gates only and (*b*) NOR gates only.

3.35 A circuit is required to produce the outputs $F_1 = AC + DB$ and $F_2 = \bar{A} + BD$. Draw a possible circuit using NAND gates only.

3.36 Implement using NAND gates only

$$F = (A + B + C)(\bar{A}\bar{C} + A\bar{B})$$

3.37 Implement using NOR gates only

$$F = ABC + \bar{A}B\bar{C}$$

3.38 A digital circuit has three inputs *A*, *B* and *C* and three outputs *X*, *Y* and *Z*. The truth table for this circuit is given by Table E.3.1. Determine the Boolean expressions for *X*, *Y* and *Z*.

Table E.3.1

A	0 1 0 1 0 1 0 1
B	0 0 1 1 0 0 1 1
C	0 0 0 0 1 1 1 1
X	1 0 0 0 0 0 1 0
Y	0 1 1 0 1 1 0 0
Z	0 0 0 1 0 0 0 1

3.39 Obtain the Boolean equation for the output *F* of the circuit whose truth table is given by Table E.3.2. Simplify the equation and then implement it using either NAND or NOR gates only.

Table E.3.2

A	0 0 0 0 1 1 1 1
B	0 0 1 1 0 0 1 1
C	0 1 0 1 0 1 0 1
F	1 1 1 0 1 0 1 0

3.40 A circuit is required that has 10 inputs, labelled 0 through to 9, and one output. The output of the circuit should go high when or more of the inputs 1, 3 and 5 are high. Write down the truth table and hence determine the Boolean equation describing the wanted circuit. Implement the circuit using either NAND or NOR gates only.

3.41 Table E.3.3 gives the truth table of a logic circuit.

Table E.3.3

A	0 1 0 1 0 1 1 0
B	0 0 0 1 1 0 1 1
C	1 0 0 0 0 1 1 1
F	1 0 0 0 0 1 1 1

Obtain the Boolean equation describing the circuit and reduce it to its simplest form.

3.42 For the circuit in **3.41** write down the Boolean equation for $\bar{F}$. Then invert it to get F.

4 Practical Electronic Gates

4.1 Figure E.4.1 shows how the collector/emitter voltage of a transistor varies when a rectangular pulse of +5 V is applied to its base terminal. Calculate (a) $V_{CE(SAT)}$, (b) the fall-time t_f, and (c) the rise time t_r of the transistor.

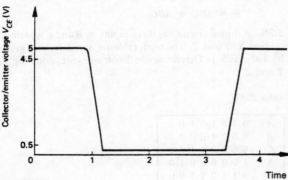

Fig. E.4.1

4.2 When a rectangular pulse is applied to the base of a transistor, Fig. E.4.2a, the resultant change in the collector/emitter voltage is as shown in Fig. E.4.2b. Give a name to both the time periods t_f and t_r and explain how they arise.

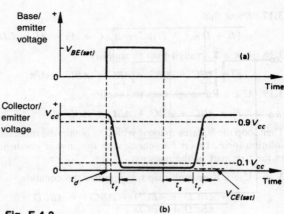

Fig. E.4.2

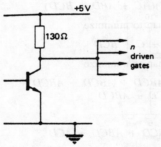

Fig. E.4.3

4.3 Figure E.4.3 shows the output circuit of a gate. If the logic 1 level is defined by the voltage limits 3.5 V to 5 V calculate the fan-out of the circuit. Assume that each of the driven gates takes a current of 1.6 mA.

4.4 The gate shown in Fig. E.4.3 is connected to four similar gates. Each gate has an input resistance of 4000 ohms. Calculate the logic 1 output voltage level.

4.5 A TTL gate has a minimum logic 1 voltage level of 2.4 V and a maximum logic 0 voltage level of 400 mV. Calculate the worst-case noise margin of the gate.

4.6 Figure E.4.4 shows the circuit of a CMOS gate. State the logical function performed by the circuit and describe its operation.

4.7 Figure E.4.5 shows the pin connections of the 4012 dual 4-input NAND gate. Show how the IC would be connected to produce the logical function $F = (A + B + C)D$.

4.8 Explain why CMOS devices require very careful handling whilst being fitted into a circuit. List the precautions you would take.

4.9 What is likely to happen if one input is left disconnected on (a) a standard TTL gate, (b) a low-power Schottky gate, (c) a CMOS gate, or (d) an ECL gate?

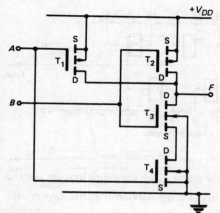

Fig. E.4.4

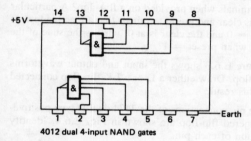

4012 dual 4-input NAND gates

Fig. E.4.5

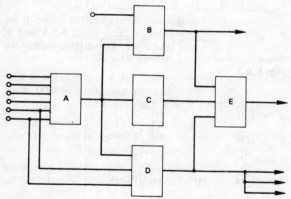

Fig. E.4.6

4.10 Referring to Fig. E.4.6. What are (*a*) the required fan-in for each gate, (*b*) the required fan-out for each gate?

4.11 Explain why power dissipation in a digital IC is of importance. If 4000 CMOS is ruled out in the grounds of speed what is then the best family in this respect?

4.12 Explain the significance of noise margin for a gate and say how it is related to the logic levels for binary 1 and 0.

4.13 Explain why a disconnected input to a TTL gate acts like a logic 1 input.

4.14 A 24-input NAND gate is to be designed using 7430 8-input NAND gate ICs. Draw a suitable circuit. If necessary, 7404 hex inverters and 7420 dual 4-input NAND gates are also available.

4.15 Explain the reasons why the AND gate, although available in the TTL and CMOS logic families, is rarely used and any wanted AND functions are produced by suitably connected NAND or NOR gates.

4.16 The logical function $F = \overline{ABC + DEF}$ is to be implemented. Draw possible arrangements using (*a*) NAND gates only, (*b*) open-collector gates only.

4.17 Figure E.4.7 shows the circuit of a CMOS gate. Describe the operation of the circuit and say what kind of gate it is.

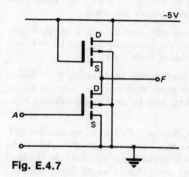

Fig. E.4.7

4.18 Implement the function $F = (\overline{AB + CD})AC$: (*a*) without simplification using either NAND or NOR gates; (*b*) simplify the equation and use NAND gates only.

4.19 Explain, with the aid of a diagram, the operation of a TTL low-power Schottky NAND circuit. Show how one or more NAND gates can be used to produce (*a*) the OR function, (*b*) the NOT function.

4.20 What is the advantage of using the wired-OR connection compared with using cascaded totem-pole output stage gates to obtain a given logical function?

4.21 What is a Schottky transistor and why is it used?

4.22 What is meant by the terms fan-in and fan-out when applied to an electronic gate?

4.23 List the relative advantages of TTL and low-power Schottky logic elements. What is the result of exceeding the fan-out of an electronic gate?

5 MSI Combinational Logic Circuits

5.1 Explain the advantage to be gained from using a MSI multiplexer IC to implement a Boolean logic equation.

5.2 Use a multiplexer to implement the function

$$F = ABC + \bar{A}D + \bar{C}D$$

5.3 Use a multiplexer to implement the function

$$F = ABCD + \bar{A}BCD + AB\bar{C}D + \bar{A}B\bar{C}D$$

5.4 Use a multiplexer to implement the Boolean equation

$$F = ABC\bar{D} + A\bar{B}\bar{C} + \bar{A}D$$

5.5 Explain how a 74138 1-of-8 demultiplexer/decoder can be operated as either a demultiplexer or a decoder.

5.6 Write down the truth table of a BCD-to-decimal decoder. Suggest a way in which two 7442 ICs can be connected to convert BCD to decimal for numbers up to 99.

5.7 Give the truth table of a full adder and then use it to outline the operation of such a circuit.

5.8 Derive a method by which two binary half adders can be combined to give one binary full adder.

5.9 Explain the reasons why circuits such as multiplexers, decoders and adders are normally employed in IC form and not in the possible random logic form.

5.10 Compare the truth tables of a multiplexer and a demultiplexer and then state, with reasons, whether or not you think a demultiplexer may be used to implement a logic function.

5.11 Draw the block diagram of a 3-to-8 line decoder and, with the aid of a truth table, explain its operation. (*a*) If the input signal is 101 which output line is selected? (*b*) If output line 7 is to be selected what should be the input signal?

6 Flip-flops

6.1 The waveform shown in Fig. E.6.1*a* is connected to the input terminal of Fig. E.6.1*b*. Draw the output waveform.

6.2 Figure E.6.2 shows the pin connections of the 4001 quad 2-input NOR gate IC. Show how it can be connected to act as a D flip-flop.

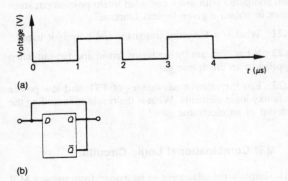

(a)

(b)

Fig. E.6.1

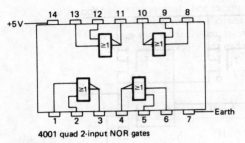

Fig. E.6.2 4001 quad 2-input NOR gates

6.3 Discuss the reasons why some flip-flops are clocked.

6.4 Why are most J-K flip-flops either master-slave or edge-triggered types?

6.5 What are the functions of (*a*) the clear and (*b*) the preset terminals when provided on a flip-flop? A particular device has clear and preset terminals that are active low. If $J = 1$, $K = 0$ and the clear is at 0, what is the state of the Q output when preset $= 1$?

6.6 Figure E.6.3 shows the input and output waveforms of a flip-flop. Draw either a D or a J-K flip-flop connected to give this result.

6.7 The pin connections of the 7474 dual D type positive-edge triggered flip-flop are shown in Fig. E.6.4. Identify the function of each pin.

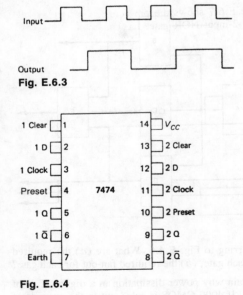

Fig. E.6.3

Fig. E.6.4

6.8 The function table of the 7474 D flip-flop is given in Table E.6.1. (*a*) If the preset input is low, does the flip-flop set whatever the state of the D and the clock inputs?

(*b*) If the preset and clear inputs are not used, should they be connected to +5 V or to 0 V? (*c*) If the *D* input is high, and the preset and clear are not used, does the flip-flop set or reset when the clock changes from 0 to 1?

Table E.6.1

Preset	Clear	Clock	D	Q'	$\bar{Q}'$
L	H	X	X	H	L
H	L	X	X	L	H
L	L	X	X	H	H
H	H	0−1	H	H	L
H	H	0−1	L	L	H
H	H	L	X	Q	$\bar{Q}$

6.9 Draw the circuit of a clocked S-R flip-flop using NAND gates. If the *S* and *R* input waveforms are as shown in Fig. 6.5 draw the output waveform if the circuit is arranged to be (*a*) leading-edge triggered and (*b*) trailing-edge triggered.

6.10 Figure E.6.6 shows the input waveforms of a J-K flip-flop. Draw the output waveforms if the circuit is (*a*) leading-edge triggered and (*b*) trailing-edge triggered.

6.11 (*a*) Show how an S-R flip-flop can be constructed using NAND gates only.
(*b*) Modify the circuit to act as a D flip-flop.
(*c*) Show how the D flip-flop circuit can be used as a clocked divide-by-two circuit.

6.12 Figure E.6.7 shows the pin connections of a 4001 CMOS quad 2-input NOR gate. Explain, with the aid of

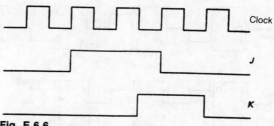

Fig. E.6.6

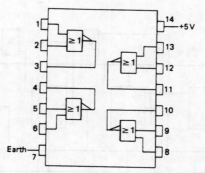

Fig. E.6.7

diagrams, how the IC could be connected to form a divide-by-two circuit. Discuss the precautions needed when handling CMOS circuits.

6.13 Show how two NOR gates may be interconnected to form an S-R flip-flop. Give a truth table for the circuit.

6.14 Explain, with the aid of a truth table, the logical operation of a master-slave J-K flip-flop. Could the circuit be modified to act as (*a*) a D flip-flop, (*b*) a T flip-flop?

6.15 Write down the truth table of a J-K flip-flop. Explain how it differs from the truth table of an S-R flip-flop. Explain how a J-K flip-flop can be used as a divide-by-two device.

6.16 A J-K flip-flop is in the state $Q = 1$, $\bar{Q} = 0$. What change in state will occur if the flip-flop is (*a*) set, (*b*) reset, (*c*) cleared, (*d*) clocked?

6.17 Why cannot a T flip-flop be purchased in integrated form? How can a T flip-flop be obtained?

7   Counters and Shift Registers

7.1 For Fig. E.7.1: (*a*) What is the count of the circuit? (*b*) Is it a synchronous or a non-synchronous circuit? (*c*) To what logic levels must (i) the *J*, (ii) the *K* inputs be connected?

7.2 Modify the circuit of Fig. E.7.2 to have a count of 6.

7.3 Explain the operation of the counter given in Fig. E.7.3.

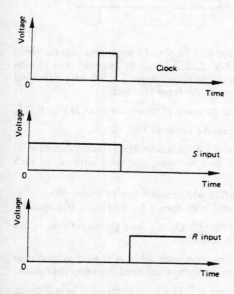

Fig. E.6.5

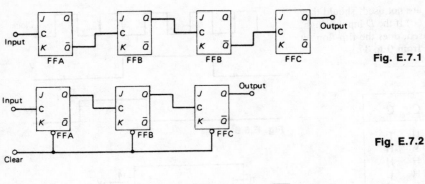

Fig. E.7.1

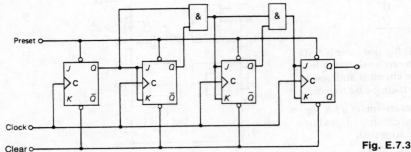

Fig. E.7.2

Fig. E.7.3

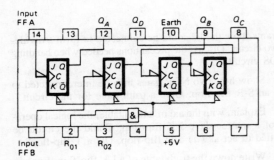

Fig. E.7.4

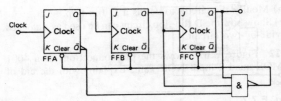

Fig. E.7.5

7.4 Figure E.7.4 shows the pin connections of the 7493 counter. The IC can be connected to operate as a divide-by-16 counter. Show the necessary connections. Also show it connected to divide-by-12.

7.5 Show how one 7490 and one 7493 IC counter can be connected together to give a count of 80. The pin connections of these devices are given in Chapter 7.

7.6 Two 7490 decade counters are to be connected to give a count of 21. Obtain the required circuit.

7.7 Three decade counters are connected together to give a count of 1000. Calculate the frequency of the output waveform when the clock frequency is 3 MHz. What is the most likely source of the clock waveform?

7.8 The 7424 hex Schmitt trigger IC has a positive-going

threshold voltage of 1.71 V and a negative-going threshold voltage of 0.88 V. Calculate (a) its hysteresis and (b) the duration of the output pulse when a 2 V 500 kHz sinusoidal signal is applied to the input terminals.

7.9 Determine the count of the circuit given in Fig. E.7.5.

7.10 Determine the count of Fig. E.7.6.

7.11 Show how a 4-bit synchronous counter can have its count reduced to 9 by using the reset terminal of each flip-flop.

7.12 The CMOS 4020 counter has 14 stages. What is its maximum count? Why does it have only 12 Q outputs?

7.13 Sketch the Q_A, Q_B, Q_C and Q_D waveforms of the counter of Fig. E.7.6.

7.14 Write down the truth table of a 4-bit synchronous counter and use it to show the need for two AND gates.

7.15 The counter of **7.13** is to be extended to have 5 stages. Sketch the extra circuitry required.

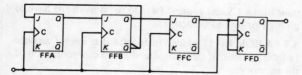

Fig. E.7.6

7.16 Draw the clock and output waveforms of a divide-by-8 counter.

7.17 Discuss the different ways in which the count of a 4-bit non-synchronous counter can have its count reduced.

7.18 Show how a number of 7493 counters can be connected to give a count of 50.

7.19 Three J-K flip-flops are connected to operate as a ripple counter. Give the counting sequence obtained at (a) the Q outputs and (b) the $\bar{Q}$ outputs.

7.20 List the relative merits of TTL and CMOS counters.

7.21 Determine (a) the maximum count and (b) the decoded count of the circuit given in Fig. E.7.7.

7.22 Determine the count of the circuit of Fig. E.7.8.

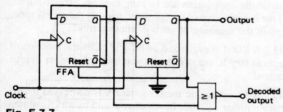

Fig. E.7.7

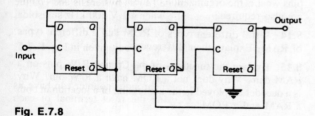

Fig. E.7.8

7.23 The CMOS 4516 is described as a presettable up-down binary counter. Explain what this means.

7.24 Several IC counters are said by the manufacturer to be synchronous counters with asynchronous clear. What does this mean?

7.25 A 5-stage ripple counter has an input clock frequency

of 1 MHz. At what frequency do the second, third and fifth stages operate?

7.26 Draw the block diagram of a 6-bit shift register using J-K flip-flops. Explain how it operates when the number 110010 is loaded (a) serially and (b) in parallel. Assume a serial output.

7.27 Explain the function of the shift mode control of a shift register.

7.28 Figure E.7.9 shows the pin connections of the CMOS 40100 32-stage shift register. State the function of each pin.

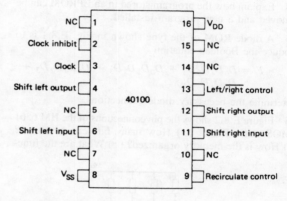

Fig. E.7.9

7.29 Figure E.7.10 shows the pin connections of the 4027 dual J-K flip-flop. Show how two of these ICs can be connected together to form a 4-bit shift register.

7.30 A shift register has 8 stages. If the clock frequency is 2 MHz calculate the time needed to load the register (a) serially and (b) in parallel.

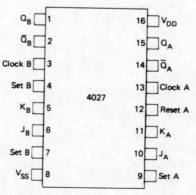

Fig. E.7.10

8 Semiconductor Memories

8.1 Define the terms static RAM and dynamic RAM. List the advantages and disadvantages of a bipolar transistor static RAM compared with a mosfet static RAM.

8.2 What is meant by the terms volatile and non-volatile when applied to a memory or store? Which type is (a) a RAM, (b) a ROM? Give one example of the use of each type of memory.

8.3 A PROM is listed as having a capacity of 256k × 4. What does this mean?

8.4 Explain how the program stored in an EPROM can be removed and a new program installed.

8.5 A diode ROM of the type shown in Fig. E.8.1 is to produce the Boolean equation

$$F = D_0 D_1 D_2 D_3 + \bar{D}_0 \bar{D}_1 \bar{D}_2 \bar{D}_3 + D_0 \bar{D}_1 \bar{D}_2 D_3 + D_0 D_1 D_2 \bar{D}_3$$

Determine the necessary diode connections.

8.6 Figure E.8.2 shows the pin connections of the HM 6561 CMOS static RAM. (a) How many bits can be stored? (b) How is the memory organized? (c) What are the func-

tions of the $\overline{CS}$ and $\bar{E}$ pins? (d) Do the pins in (c) have to go high or low to be active?

8.7 A ROM has 11 address lines and 8 data lines. Calculate (a) the number of bits stored and (b) the organization of the memory.

8.8 Figure E.8.3 shows the basic block diagram of a 1024 × 1 RAM. Draw a diagram to show how 4 such RAMs could be connected to give a 1024 × 4 memory.

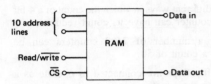

Fig. E.8.3

8.9 A ROM has 12 address lines. Calculate the number of memory locations.

8.10 The main factors affecting the choice of a RAM for a particular application are (a) the memory size required, (b) the organization of the memory, and (c) the access time. Explain the meaning of each of these terms.

8.11 A ROM is organized as 8k × 8. List the function of the necessary IC pins. What is the minimum number of pins required?

8.12 A 64-bit square memory matrix is addressed by the binary number 110100. In which row and in which column is the wanted location?

8.13 A RAM has 4096 addressable locations. How many address pins does it have? If there are four data input/output pins what is the organization of the RAM? What other pins are also required?

8.14 List 3 different types of ROM and 2 different types of RAM. Explain their differences.

8.15 Explain the functions of the $\overline{CS}$ and R/$\overline{W}$ pins on a RAM chip. Why does not a ROM have a R/$\overline{W}$ pin? Why is a decoder employed in the addressing of a location in both a RAM and a ROM?

8.16 Draw a ROM to implement the Boolean functions

$$F = ABCD + A\bar{B}C\bar{D} + \bar{A}\bar{B}\bar{C}D + AB\bar{C}\bar{D}$$
$$F = A\bar{B} + \bar{A}B$$

8.17 Determine the Boolean equation that is held by the ROM given in Fig. E.8.4.

8.18 Outline, with the aid of a block diagram, the principle of operation of a PLA. What is meant by the terms mask-programmable and field-programmable?

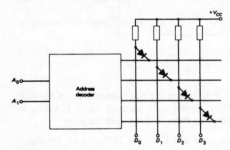

Fig. E.8.1

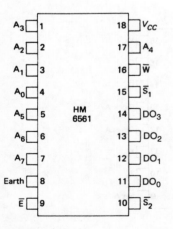

Fig. E.8.2

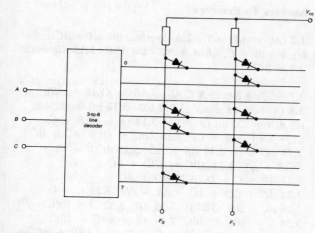

Fig. E.8.4

8.19 Design a PLA to implement the equations given in **8.16**.

8.20 Design a PLA to implement $F = ABC + BCD + ACD + ABD$.

9 Visual Displays

9.1 Write down the truth table for a BCD-to-7-segment decoder, assuming a luminous segment is illuminated by the logic 1 state. Use it to obtain Boolean expressions for the decimal numbers 5 and 9.

9.2 Answer the following questions relating to an LCD display:

(a) Can the display be read in the dark?
(b) Will the display work in very low ambient temperatures?
(c) Is the display affected if it is situated in very bright sunlight?

Give reasons for your answers.

9.3 What is meant by multiplexing when applied to a 6-digit LED display? State one disadvantage and one advantage of using multiplexing.

9.4 An LED is to be connected between the output of a TTL device and +5 V. Determine the value of the series current-limiting resistor required. The LED ON voltage is 1.6 V and the low output voltage of the TTL circuit is 0.2 V. Find also the power dissipated in the series resistance. Assume the safe LED current to be 20 mA.

9.5 Draw a 16-segment display and state which segments must be lit for the display to indicate (a) 4, (b) A, (c) R, and (d) T.

9.6 Explain the principle of operation of a dot matrix alphanumeric display, using the letter S as an example.

9.7 A dot matrix liquid crystal display module contains an LCD display and a CMOS LSI drive unit. If the module is operated in conjunction with an LSI controller with on-chip character generator all the ASCII characters can be displayed. Discuss the merits of using such a module.

9.8 Briefly explain the action of a LED. List four advantages and two disadvantages of the LED as a display device.

10 Analogue-to-Digital and Digital-to-Analogue Converters

10.1 Explain, with the aid of a block diagram, the difference between a digital-to-analogue converter and an analogue-to-digital converter.

10.2 Most DACs are of either the binary weighted resistor, or the $R/2R$ type. What are the disadvantages of the former and when might it be employed?

10.3 Figure E.10.1 is the basic circuit of an 8-bit successive approximation ADC. Explain its action.

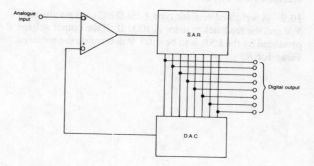

Fig. E.10.1

10.4 The maximum input voltage to a successive approximation ADC is 5 V. Calculate the voltage corresponding to the LSB if (a) 8 bits and (b) 16 bits are used. Hence compare the circuits on a basis of both speed and noise.

10.5 An 8-bit DAC of the binary weighted type uses a lowest resistor value of 1 kΩ. Calculate the values required for the other resistors. Comment on your answer.

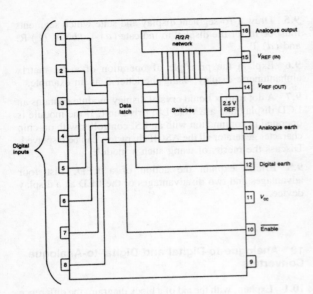

Fig. E.10.2

10.6 The internal connections of the ZN588E DAC are shown by Fig. E.10.2. Explain the operation of the IC.

10.7 The resolution of an n-bit DAC is equal to 2^n. Deterine the resolution of (a) an 8-bit and (b) a 12-bit DAC expressed as (i) a percentage of the LSB, (ii) in PPM.

10.8 An analogue signal of peak voltage $+5$ V is applied to a successive approximation ADC. Sketch the output voltage of the circuit.

10.9 A weighted resistor type 4-bit DAC uses a voltage of 5 V and the feedback resistor is 1000 Ω. If the output voltage produced by the LSB is to be 0.05 V determine the required value for R.

Answers To Exercises

2.2 $(A\bar{B} + \bar{A}B) + C$ **2.4** (a) $\overline{ABC}$, (b) $A\bar{B} + A\bar{C}$, (c) $\bar{A} + \bar{B} + \bar{C}$, (d) $A + BC$ **2.6** $\bar{A}BC$ **2.15** $AB + C$, $AB + BC$

3.1 $\bar{A}BC$ **3.2** 0 **3.3** $C(AB + \bar{A}\bar{B}) + \bar{C}(A\bar{B} + \bar{A}B)$
3.6 $(A + B)(A + C)$ **3.9** 0,1,0 **3.11** (a) 0, (b) AB,
(c) $A(B + \bar{C})$, (d) $(\bar{A} + \bar{C})$ **3.14** $(A + \bar{C})(\bar{B} + \bar{C})$
$(A + \bar{B})(\bar{A} + B + C)$ **3.15** $\bar{A}BC + A\bar{B} + A\bar{C} + \bar{B}C$
3.18 $AC + \bar{B}$ **3.19** $AB + \bar{A}\bar{C}$ **3.20** $AC(\bar{B} + D) +$
$\bar{A}\bar{C}(B + \bar{D})$ **3.21** $ABC + AB\bar{D} + \bar{B}\bar{C}$
3.22 $A\bar{B} + C + D$ **3.23** $BD + \bar{B}\bar{D}$
3.24 $\bar{A}C + \bar{C}D + A\bar{C} + \bar{A}\bar{B} + \bar{B}D$ **3.25** $C + D$
3.26 $BC + BD$ **3.27** 0 **3.28** AB **3.32** $(\bar{A} + \bar{B})(\bar{C} + \bar{D})$
3.38 $X = \bar{A}\bar{B}\bar{C} + \bar{A}BC$, $Y = A\bar{B} + \bar{A}B\bar{C} + \bar{A}\bar{B}C$,
$Z = AB$ **3.39** $F = A\bar{B} + \bar{C}$ **3.40** $F = AB\bar{D} + AB\bar{C}\bar{D}$
3.41 $F = C$

4.1 0.2 V, 150 ns, 300 ns **4.3** 7 **4.4** 4.425 V
4.5 400 mV **4.10** A:6, 3;B:2, 2;C:1, 1;D:3, 4;E:3, 1

6.5 0 **6.8** (a) yes, (b) $+5$ V, (c) set **6.16** (a) none,
(b) $Q=0$, (c) $Q =0$, (d) depends on J and K

7.1 (a) 15, (b) none, (c) 1,1 **7.7** 3 kHz **7.8** 0.83 V,
528 ns **7.9** 6 **7.10** 5 (irregular sequence)
7.12 16383 **7.21** 3,0 **7.22** 6 **7.25** 500 kHz, 250 kHz,
62.5 kHz **7.30** (a) 4 μS, (b) 0.5μS

8.6 (a) 1024, (b) 256 × 4, (c) 2048 × 8
8.7 (a) 16384, (b) 2048 × 8 **8.9** 4096 **8.11** 24

9.4 160 Ω, 64 mW

10.4 19.53 mV, 76.3 μV **10.7** (a) 0.3906, 3906,
(b) 0.0244, 244 **10.9** 1562 Ω

Appendix A

The various logic families all offer circuits such as gates, inverters, flip-flops, encoders/multiplexers, decoders/ demultiplexers, comparators, counters, shift registers, bus drivers and transceivers, display decoders/drivers, and adders. Very often a particular circuit is available in several different logic families. Some examples of the ICs listed in one distributor's catalogue are given in Table A.1.

Table A.1

Type	Function	Std	LS	ALS	F	AS	HC	HCT	AC	ACT	BCT
00	Quad 2-input NAND gate	√	√	√	√	√	√	√	√	√	–
02	Quad 2-input AND gate	√	√	√	√	√	√	√	–	–	–
04	Hex inverter	√	√	√	√	√	√	√	–	√	–
74	Dual D edge-triggered flip-flop	√	√	√	√	√	√	√	√	√	–
90	Decade non-synchronous counter	√	√	–	–	–	–	–	–	–	–
137	Demultiplexer	–	√	–	–	–	√	√	–	√	–
161	Binary synchronous counter	√	√	√	√	√	√	√	√	√	–
240	Octal bus driver	–	√	√	√	√	√	√	√	√	√

Note: STD = standard, LS = low-power Schottky, ALS = advanced low-power Schottky, AS = advanced Schottky, F = FAST, HC = high-speed CMOS, HCT = high-speed CMOS with TTL inputs, AC = advanced CMOS, ACT = advanced CMOS with TTL inputs, and BCT = BiCMOS.

The device numbers and the pin-outs of similar devices in the listed logic families are in agreement with the numbers and pin-outs of the TTL devices. In general, only the 4000 series CMOS and ECL devices use a different numbering system. Pin-outs of some TTL and some CMOS gates are shown in Fig. A.1.

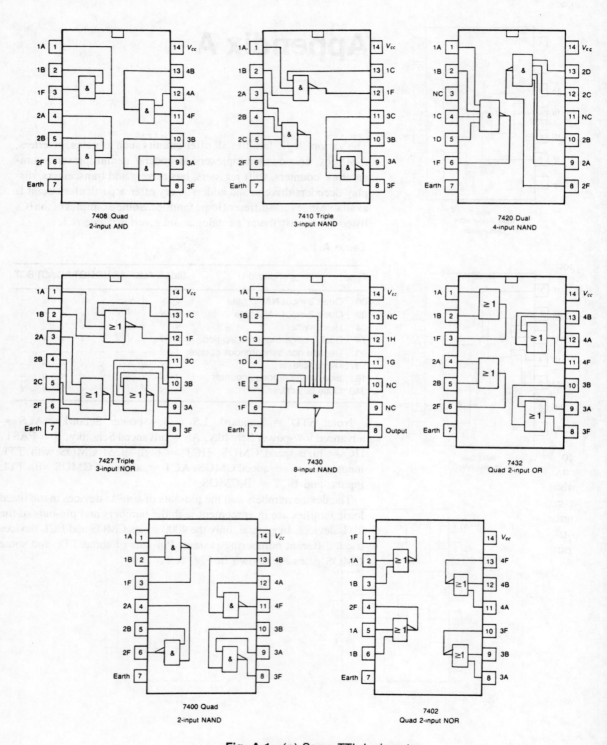

Fig. A.1   (*a*) Some TTL logic gates

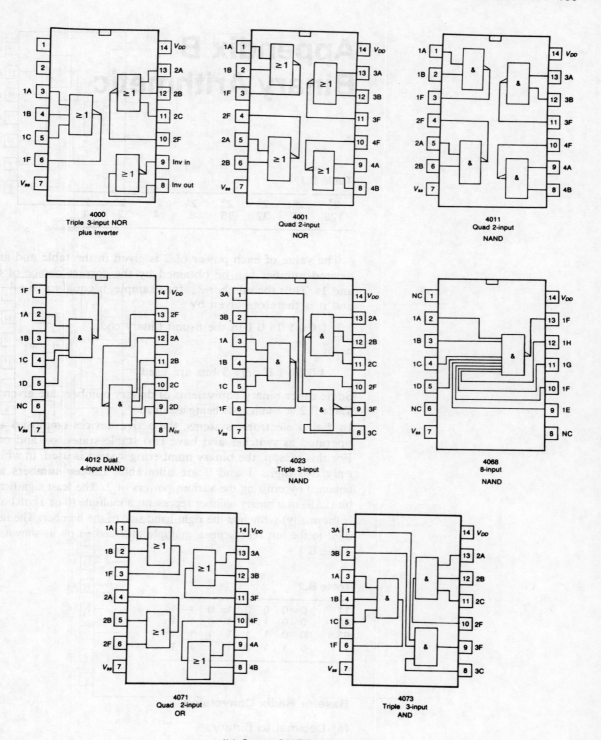

(b) Some CMOS logic gates

Appendix B
Binary Arithmetic

Table B.1

2^7	2^6	2^5	2^4	2^3	2^2	2^1	2^0
128	64	32	16	8	4	2	1

The value of each power of 2 is given in the table and any desired number can be obtained by the correct choice of 0s and 1s. Thus the number 21, for example, is equal to $16+4+1$ and it is therefore given by

00010101 in the 8-unit binary code

or by

10101 if only 5 bits are used

Some other binary equivalents of denary numbers are given in Table B.2, a 7-unit code being assumed.

In digital electronic systems, the active devices employed are operated as switches and have two stable states, ON and OFF. For this reason, the binary numbering system is used, in which only two digits 1 and 0 are allowable. Larger numbers are obtained by utilizing the various powers of 2. The least significant bit (LSB) of a binary number represents a multiple (0 or 1) of 1 and is (normally) written at the right-hand side of the number. The next digit to the left represents a multiple of 2 and so on as shown by Table B.1.

Table B.2

11	0	0	0	0	1	0	1	1
43	0	0	1	0	1	0	1	1
63	0	0	1	1	1	1	1	1
111	0	1	1	0	1	1	1	1

Base or Radix Conversion

(a) Decimal to Binary

To convert a decimal integer number into its binary equivalent, the decimal number should be repeatedly divided by 2, and each time the remainder, which will be either 0 or 1, should be recorded. Eventually the number will be reduced to 1, at which stage further division will not give an integer number, and so the quotient 1 is considered to be a remainder of 1. The required binary number is then obtained by writing down the remainders in reverse order.

EXAMPLE 1

Convert 38 into binary.

Solution
number   38   19   9   4   2   1
remainder   0   1   1   0   0   1
Therefore   38 = 100110

EXAMPLE 2

Convert 277 into binary.

Solution
number   277   138   69   34   17   8   4   2   1
remainder   1   0   1   0   1   0   0   0   1
Therefore   277 = 100010101

(b) Decimal Fractions to Binary Fractions

To convert a decimal fractional number into the corresponding binary fraction, multiply the decimal fraction repeatedly by 2 and each time record the integer number obtained. The required binary fraction is then obtained by reading the integers from left to right.

EXAMPLE 3

Convert 0.426 to binary.

Solution
fraction   0.426   0.852   1.714   1.428   0.856   1.712   1.424
integers   0   1   1   0   1   1   etc.
Therefore   0.426 = 0.011011 etc.

EXAMPLE 4

Convert 0.125 into binary.

Solution
fraction   0.125   0.25   0.5   1.0
integers   0   0   1
Therefore   0.125 = 0.001

(c) Binary to Denary

The conversion of binary numbers into their denary equivalents is best achieved using either Table B.1 or Table B.3.

Table B.3

2^{-1}	2^{-2}	2^{-3}	2^{-4}	2^{-5}
0.5	0.25	0.125	0.0625	0.03125

EXAMPLE 5

Convert 10110.101 into denary.

Solution
Using Tables 1 and 2,
10110.101
$$= 1\times16+0\times8+1\times4+1\times2+0\times1+1\times0.5+0\times0.25+1\times0.125$$
$$= 22.625$$

Arithmetic Operations

The processes of binary addition, subtraction, multiplication and division are essentially the same as in ordinary base 10 arithmetic but are, of course, restricted to the use of the two digits 1 and 0.

(a) Binary Addition

The rules for the addition of binary numbers are given by Table B.4.

When two 1s are added together their sum is 10 and so the sum in that order of unit is 0 with a carry of 1.

Table B.4

A	B	Sum	Carry
0	0	0	0
1	0	1	0
0	1	1	0
1	1	0	1

EXAMPLE 6

Add the binary numbers 10111 and 01101.

Solution
$$\begin{aligned}
1\,0\,1\,1\,1 &= 23 \\
+\,0\,1\,1\,0\,1 &= 13 \\
\hline
1\,0\,0\,1\,0\,0 &= 36
\end{aligned}$$

(b) Binary Subtraction

The rules for performing binary subtraction are given in Table B.5.

When a number is to be subtracted from a smaller number (always $0-1$), a 1 must be borrowed from the next column to the left. This 1 is a power of 2 higher and hence the subtraction becomes $2-1=1$.

Table B.5

A	B	Difference	Borrow
0	0	0	0
1	0	1	0
0	1	1	1
1	1	0	0

EXAMPLE 7

Subtract 10101 from 11011.

Solution

$$\begin{array}{r} 1\,1\,0\,1\,1=27 \\ -1\,0\,1\,0\,1=21 \\ \hline 0\,0\,1\,1\,0=\ \ 6 \end{array}$$

EXAMPLE 8

Subtract 111010 from 1011111.

Solution

$$\begin{array}{r} 1\,0\,1\,1\,1\,1\,1=95 \\ -1\,1\,1\,0\,1\,0=58 \\ \hline 1\,0\,0\,1\,0\,1=37 \end{array}$$

The subtraction of binary numbers is more easily carried out electronically when an alternative method of subtraction is employed. A binary number has two *complements*, known as the ones complement and the twos complement. The ones complement of a binary number is obtained by changing all the 1s in the number into 0s and all the 0s into 1s. The twos complement is obtained by adding 1 to the 1s complement.

The subtraction of a number x from another number y is achieved in the following way. The ones or the twos complement of x is obtained and is then *added* to y. If the left-hand digit of the sum is 0, the difference is *negative*; conversely, if the left-hand digit is 1, a positive difference has been obtained. This left-hand digit is known as the *sign* digit since it indicates the sign ($\pm$) of the difference.

When the sign digit is 0, the result is negative and the complement of the difference is obtained. When the sign digit is 1, the result of adding y to the complement of x actually is the required difference when the twos complement has been used. When the ones complement has been used, the required difference *minus* 1 is obtained; in this case the positive sign digit 1 must be shifted around to the right-hand side of the number and *added* to the digit already there.

EXAMPLE 9

Subtract 10101 from 11011 using the twos complement method.

Solution

$$
\begin{array}{r}
1\,1\,0\,1\,1 = 27 \\
-1\,0\,1\,0\,1 = 21
\end{array}
=
\begin{array}{l}
1\,1\,0\,1\,1 \\
+0\,1\,0\,1\,1 \quad \text{twos complement} \\
\hline
1\,0\,0\,1\,1\,0 = +6
\end{array}
$$

EXAMPLE 10

Subtract 11011 from 10101 using the twos complement method.

Solution

$$
\begin{array}{r}
1\,0\,1\,0\,1 = 21 \\
-1\,1\,0\,1\,1 = 27
\end{array}
=
\begin{array}{l}
1\,0\,1\,0\,1 \\
+0\,0\,1\,0\,1 \quad \text{twos complement} \\
\hline
\text{negative sign} \rightarrow 0\,1\,1\,0\,1\,0
\end{array}
$$

The ones complement is $11010-1$ or 11001 and so the required difference is

$$0\,0\,1\,1\,0 = -6$$

EXAMPLE 11

Subtract 11101 from 01011 using the twos complement method.

Solution

$$
\begin{array}{r}
0\,1\,0\,1\,1 = 11 \\
-1\,1\,1\,0\,1 = 29
\end{array}
=
\begin{array}{l}
0\,1\,0\,1\,1 \\
+0\,0\,0\,1\,1 \quad \text{twos complement} \\
\hline
\text{negative sign} \rightarrow 0\,0\,1\,1\,1\,0
\end{array}
$$

The ones complement is 01101 and so the required difference is

$$1\,0\,0\,1\,0 = -18$$

EXAMPLE 12

Subtract 11101 from 01011 using the ones complement method.

Solution

$$
\begin{array}{r}
0\,1\,0\,1\,1 = 11 \\
-1\,1\,1\,0\,1 = 29
\end{array}
=
\begin{array}{l}
0\,1\,0\,1\,1 \\
+0\,0\,0\,1\,0 \quad \text{ones complement} \\
\hline
0\,0\,1\,1\,0\,1
\end{array}
$$

and so the difference is

$$1\,0\,0\,1\,0 = -18$$

EXAMPLE 13

Subtract 01011 from 11101 using the ones complement method.

Solution

$$
\begin{array}{rl}
11101=29 \\
-01011=11
\end{array} =
\begin{array}{l}
11101 \\
+10100 \quad \text{ones complement} \\
\hline
110001
\end{array}
$$

The positive sign digit (1) must now be shifted around to the right-hand side of the number and added to the digit already there. Hence the difference is

$$10010 = 18$$

(c) Binary Multiplication

The product of two binary numbers is 1 only if both the digits are 1. Otherwise it is 0.

EXAMPLE 14

Multiply 11011 by 10101.

Solution

$$
\begin{array}{r}
11011=27 \\
\times 10101=21 \\
\hline
11011 \\
00000 \\
11011 \\
00000 \\
11011 \\
\hline
1000110111=1+2+4+16+32+512 \\
=567
\end{array}
$$

(d) Binary Division

Binary division is carried out in the same way as the more customary denary division.

EXAMPLE 15

Divide 11011 by 01001.

Solution

$$
\begin{array}{r}
11 \\
01001{\overline{\smash{)}\,11011}} \\
1001 \\
\hline
1001 \\
1001 \quad =11=3 \\
\hline
0000
\end{array}
$$

Index